DISTRIBUTIONS

DISTRIBUTIONS

An Outline

by

JEAN-PAUL MARCHAND

Institute of Physics, University of Geneva

WITH A FOREWORD

by

ANDRÉ MERCIER

*Professor of theoretical Physics, University
of Bern*

1962

NORTH-HOLLAND PUBLISHING COMPANY / AMSTERDAM

INTERSCIENCE PUBLISHERS INC. / NEW YORK

PUBLISHERS:

NORTH-HOLLAND PUBLISHING COMPANY / AMSTERDAM

SOLE DISTRIBUTORS U.S.A.:

INTERSCIENCE PUBLISHERS INC. / NEW YORK

PRINTED IN THE NETHERLANDS

FOREWORD

Distributions are mathematical entities very useful in various fields; e.g. each time functions may be distributed in a space with a prescribed density, a 'distribution' can be defined correspondingly. Yet not all distributions have a regular 'density'. Precisely such distributions that may be said to be odd, singular or, if one pleases pathological call for special attention, for where, on the one hand, there is a density in the ordinary sense, integrals of functions correspondingly distributed present neither conceptual nor special mathematical difficulties, and the use of an elaborate theory of distributions seems superfluous whereas, on the other hand, if the distribution does not admit of non-singular densities, difficulties arise, the elimination of which requires elaborate mathematical considerations.

Instances of odd distributions had been discovered before a mathematically sound theory had been developed for such difficult cases. The famous Dirac measure, often named Dirac's 'delta function' (though we should not call it a function) now known to every theoretician of atomic physics, is one instance and, indeed, the most important one. In spite of not possessing a mathematically satisfactory theory, people did not trouble too much and obtained many results by calculation with Dirac's measure. This 'confidence' in a symbolic method that worked even if it was ill-founded reminds us of Heaviside's confidence when he discovered what is now known as Heaviside's calculus, though mathematicians in his day claimed it was a scandalous procedure.

As far as we know, the idea of using a thing like a 'delta-function' was first put forward by Paul Hertz in his article on Statistical Mechanics for Weber and Ganz's 'Repertorium der Physik'.[1]) However, he did not elaborate it very far, and everybody agrees to give Dirac the credit of its definitive introduction into mathematical physics. Indeed, it was he who made first an extensive use of it in his famous *Principles of Quantum Mechanics*[2]) after having stated its main properties:

$$\int_{\infty}^{\infty} \delta(x)\mathrm{d}x = 1, \quad \delta(x) = 0 \text{ (for } x \neq 0\text{), etc.}$$

Dirac was aware of the necessity to found the introduction of this new singular function on solid grounds but simultaneously he felt the power which is concealed in its symbolic use. Everyone should take the trouble to read Dirac's original work or at least an equivalent presentation of this matter in one of the many textbooks since published on Quantum Theory. However, none of these textbooks go into details as to its correct foundation, so one has to consult special literature on the subject. Unfortunately the few presentations of it published up till now are not all easy, nor are they all short, so the publication of the present little book will be welcome. For it gives in a condensed way a good deal of the essential knowledge required.

We owe the foundation of Distribution Theory to Laurent Schwartz[3]) who, following an admirable tradition of French mathematicians, conceived of the rigorous mathematical

[1]) Cf. R. H. WEBER und R. GANZ, *Repertorium der Physik*, 1. Band, 2. Teil (Leipzig und Berlin, 1916), page 503 ss.

[2]) P. A. M. DIRAC, *The Principles of Quantum Mechanics*. First edition (Oxford University, Press, 1930), section 22. (Also 3d ed., 1947, section 15.)

[3]) L. SCHWARTZ, *Théorie des Distributions* (2 volumes, Paris, 1950). The first paper published by Schwartz on these topics goes back to 1945.

frame where these outlaws found their righteous constitution.

The greatest difficulty encountered with most singular 'densities', as delta-like ones are, is perhaps the breaking-down of differentiability in the usual sense. The theory of distributions has mastered it: Distributions, as defined mathematical entities, are indefinitely differentiable. Of course, this assumes a suitable definition of the derivative of a distribution, which derivative itself shall be a distribution. Distributions appear thus as being integrals and derivatives as well of other distributions. This is very important and suggests why distributions allow a powerful generalization of Calculus and help towards the problem of solving differential equations, especially with regard to singular solutions.

We think it very commendable for a physicist in our days to learn the main features of that theory. Of course this applies still more to the mathematician. But the Author of this little book had first physicists or, let us say, applied scientists in mind as his potential readers when he wrote it, contenting himself with rendering the main features without, however, letting mathematical rigour be wanted. His presentation is attractive, yet condensed, for he does not spend many words of comment. Therefore the reader who is not yet aware of the subject-matter will have to concentrate his thoughts, for no room is wasted on details or many suggestions for physical analogies and interpretation. So there is quite a lot to find in there, but the reader will have to find part of it by himself—and that is quite an exciting task.

ANDRÉ MERCIER

PREFACE

The aim of this work is to expound in a simple but nevertheless mathematically coherent way the basis of the theories elaborated by Schwartz (chapter I) and by Mikusinski (chapter II) in distributions.

To combine this simplicity with mathematical coherence means that we shall confine ourselves to a development of the theory under simplified conditions, retaining from elaborating it in its greatest generality. The reader will find suggestions to some easy generalisations which might serve to treat a greater number of problems. The utility of the various distribution theories rests on the fact that they are theories of differentiation, characterized by the following:

(a) these theories attribute in a unique manner a distribution to all the common functions (whether they are differentiable in the usual sense or not);

(b) all the distributions are indefinitely differentiable, the derivatives being also distributions;

(c) the differentiation is a continuous operation in the space of distributions (this simplifies the questions of commutativity of the differentiation with operations such as $\sum$, $\int$, $\mathscr{F}$);

(d) each distribution is differentiated to a finite order from a continuous function.

The study of these theories has opened a vast new field of pure mathematics. If we demonstrate two of these theories, it would be enough to show how much the theories of differentiation can differ one from the other. In fact Schwartz defines his distributions as being linear and continuous functionals of a certain class of functions that are indefinitely differentiable, while Mikusinski and Erdélyi on the other hand base their work on a theorem of algebra that permits them to define the set of distributions as an extension of an algebraic ring which is essentially made up of continuous functions. It is interesting to note that any one using both methods will, approximately, arrive at the same results; however, an exact relation between the two is rather difficult to establish. This will not be done here.

With the distributions we obtain a great number of new elements not being functions, as, for example, the distributions of the type of Dirac measures and their derivatives. From this follows also that distribution theory furnishes a rigorous method for solving differential equations involving things like point-sources, line-densities etc. It is well known that the treatment of these problems—of utmost importance in Physics—shows itself to be complicated and artificiated in classical formalism.

Let the physicist who reads this booklet be warned not to expect many applications along these lines. Applications (of a rather brief form) will be made only at those points in which they can serve as illustrations of the theoretical reasoning.

The logical structure of the theories expounded in this book is persuasive in its simplicity. This was my main aim: to present this structure in the clearest and simplest way possible.

I should like to express my gratitude to Professor André Mercier, Head of the Department of theoretical Physics at Bern University, who was my teacher. He suggested that this booklet be written, helped towards its completion and gave me the support of the Department's staff. My thanks are especially due to Mrs. T. Debrunner who prepared the manuscript for the Press and to Mr. Noguerola, who rendered the text in English from the original notes written in French.

JEAN–PAUL MARCHAND

CONTENTS

NOTATION

We use the following logical symbols:

  $\triangleright$ *implies*

  $\triangleleft$ *is implied by*

  $\bowtie$ *if and only if*

  [$\cdots$] *under the assumption that* (occurs only on the right-hand side of a theorem or an equation)

Example:
$$a > 0 \quad \triangleright \quad \lambda a > 0 \quad [\lambda > 0]$$

means: from $a > 0$ follows $\lambda a > 0$ under the assumption that λ is positive.

Other example:
$$y_i \to 0 \quad [i \to \infty]$$

means: y_i converges towards 0 if i tends to ∞, which could also be written
$$i \to \infty \quad \triangleright \quad y_i \to 0 .$$

When functions $f(x)$ are considered as elements of a function-space we write either f or, when we want to indicate the variable on which f depends: $\{f(x)\}$. Transforms in the function-space by an operator A are denoted either by Af or $\{(Af)\,(y)\}$ when the independent variable is indicated (y). Examples:

$$\text{Fourier transform:}\ f \Rightarrow \mathscr{F}f = \{\,(\mathscr{F}f)\,(y)\,\}$$

$$\text{Laplace transform:}\ f \Rightarrow \mathscr{L}f = \{\,(\mathscr{L}f)\,(s)\,\}.$$

Further remarks on notation will be inserted when used.

CHAPTER I

FUNCTIONAL THEORY OF DISTRIBUTIONS

1. Mathematical preliminaries

The notions of functional analysis introduced in this section serve as a basis necessary to the understanding of the chapter.

By a 'linear space' we are to understand the set L of elements $a, b, c, \ldots$ satisfying the laws of a vector space:

(1) to two elements $a, b \in L$ we can associate a third, $c =$ '$a + b$' $\in L$ called the 'sum of a and b';

(2) $a + (b + c) = (a + b) + c$ (associative law);

(3) there exists a neutral element '0' $\in L$ such that $a + 0 = 0 + a = a$;

(4) there exists an inverse element '$-a$' $\in L$ to every a such that $a + (-a) = 0$ for all $a \in L$;

(5) $a + b = b + a$ (commutative law).

(1') let α be a complex number, then to each $a \in L$ we can associate another element c such that $c =$ 'αa' $\in L$ called the 'product of a by α'.

(2') $\alpha(a + b) = \alpha a + \alpha b$;

(3') $(\alpha + \beta)a = \alpha a + \beta a$;

(4') $\alpha(\beta a) = (\alpha\beta)a$;

(5') $1a = a$.

We also have the following relations:

$$0a = 0;$$
$$(-1)a = -a;$$
$$\alpha a + \beta b \in L \quad [a, b \in L \text{ and } \alpha, \beta \text{ are complex numbers}].$$

Let L and $\tilde{L}$ be two linear spaces and let also $\tilde{L} = A(L)$ be a unique mapping of L in $\tilde{L}$. Now if the relation

$$A(\alpha a + \beta b) = \alpha A(a) + \beta A(b) \tag{1}$$

holds where $a,b \in L$ and α,β are complex, then the mapping is called a 'linear mapping'.

The mapping A is said to be a 'functional' if the domain L is made up of the functions $\varphi, \psi, \ldots$ and the range $\tilde{L} = A(L)$ of the complex numbers $A(\varphi), A(\psi), \ldots$.

The set of linear functionals A on a linear space L is itself a linear space and known as the 'dual L' of L'; we have only to define

$$(\alpha A + \beta B)(\varphi) = \alpha \cdot A(\varphi) + \beta \cdot B(\varphi) \tag{2}$$

for all functions $\varphi \in L$.

Before introducing some examples of linear spaces and functionals of which we shall make use later, we introduce now the idea of support:

The 'support K of a function in R_n' is defined as the smallest closed sub-set in R_n and outside of which the function vanishes. The support is said to be 'compact' if in addition it is bounded. (For more elaborate details the reader is referred to any modern treatise on analysis.)

We define now the support of a functional A. To this end consider the greatest open sub-set O of R_n with the property $A(\varphi) = 0$ for all functions φ with compact support contained in O. The complement K of O in R_n is then called the 'support of the functional A'.

We are now ready to take a closer look at some examples of linear function-spaces and their duals. The set of all the functions $\varphi, \psi, \ldots$ which are defined in the euclidean space R_n (which is itself a linear space of n dimensions in which the elements are none other than the position vectors) is a linear space, and will be denoted by $\overline{\mathscr{E}}(R_n)$ if in this space are defined

$$(\varphi + \psi)\,(x) = \varphi(x) + \psi(x)$$

$$(\alpha\varphi)\,(x) = \alpha \cdot \varphi(x)$$

i.e. an addition and a multiplication respectively.

Furthermore we shall make use of the following (linear) sub-spaces of $\overline{\mathscr{E}}$:

$\mathscr{E}(R_n)$ composed of all indefinitely differentiable functions;

$\mathscr{S}(R_n)$ composed of all indefinitely differentiable 'rapidly decreasing' functions

i.e. for which (written in one dimension):

$$\lim_{|x| \to \infty} \left| x^k \frac{\mathrm{d}^m}{\mathrm{d}x^m} \varphi(x) \right| = 0 \quad \text{[all positive } k, m] \;;$$

$\mathscr{D}(R_n)$ composed of all indefinitely differentiable functions with compact support. (3)

We may now define linear functionals on these linear spaces. Thus

$$A_1(\varphi) \overset{\text{def}}{=} f(x) \frac{\mathrm{d}^m}{\mathrm{d}x^m} \varphi(x) \bigg|_{x=x_0}$$

(4)

$$A_2(\varphi) \overset{\text{def}}{=} \int_{-\infty}^{\infty} f(x) \frac{\mathrm{d}^m}{\mathrm{d}x^m} \varphi(x)\, \mathrm{d}x$$

where $f(x)$ is an arbitrary continuous function, A_1 and A_2 are two linear functionals, the first defined in whole space $\mathscr{E}$ and the second only in $\mathscr{D} \subset \mathscr{E}$.

The sets of functionals $A(\mathscr{E})$, $A(\mathscr{S})$, $A(\mathscr{D})$ form a dual linear space to $\mathscr{E}, \mathscr{S}, \mathscr{D}$ respectively, if we take into consideration def. (2). (Later on we shall denote these sets by $\mathscr{E}'$, $\mathscr{S}'$, $\mathscr{D}'$ in case they are also continuous.)

We now consider the question of *convergence in a linear space*. Let us take, for example, the convergence of a series of functions $\varphi_i(x) \in \mathscr{D}$ towards a function $\varphi(x) \in \mathscr{D}$. The problem becomes difficult if we do not make restrictions regarding the supports K_i of the functions φ_i. However, even if we suppose that all K_i are contained in a fixed K, there still exists the possibility of different definitions for the convergence of φ_i. In fact one could just demand the uniform convergence of the φ_i with respect to K (and also to the complete space R_n) in the usual sense, this is the same as asking for the convergence towards zero of the 'norms' of $(\varphi_i - \varphi)$, these being defined by

$$N(\varphi_i - \varphi) = \| \varphi_i - \varphi \| = \sup_x | \varphi_i(x) - \varphi(x) | .$$

But we could as well ask not only for the uniform convergence of the functions φ_i but of their partial derivatives $D^m \varphi_i$ which gives us the norm

$$N(\varphi_i - \varphi) = \sup_x \sum_\alpha | D^\alpha [\varphi_i(x) - \varphi(x)] | .$$

Unfortunately one should take note that our postulate of simplicity as regards the mathematical rigour, leads here to serious restrictions with respect to the generality of the problem at hand. For we are now forced to consider those topologies sufficiently simple as to permit us to extract from them only the usual definitions of convergence; be it the convergence of complex numbers, or of 'points' x_i in R_n, or even the uniform convergence of the functions and their derivatives. These definitions will be introduced as the need for them arises.

In closing let us introduce the terms *continuous mapping* and *dense subset*.

Let L and $\tilde{L}$ be two linear spaces and A any mapping of L into $\tilde{L}$. The image of a series of elements $a_i \in L$ in $\tilde{L}$ is given in this case by the elements $\tilde{a}_i = A(a_i) \in \tilde{L}$. Now once the idea of convergence in the spaces L and L' has been established and if furthermore $a_i \in L$ converges towards $a \in L$ the question then arises whether $A(a_i) = \tilde{a}_i \in \tilde{L}$ converges towards the image $A(a) \in \tilde{L}$ of a. If this be the case, that is if from

$$a_i \in L \xrightarrow{L} a \in L$$

it follows that

$$A(a_i) \in \tilde{L} \xrightarrow{\tilde{L}} A(a) \in \tilde{L} , \tag{5}$$

then the mapping A of L into $\tilde{L}$ is called 'continuous at $a \in L$'.

Here A is not necessarily linear; but if it were, it is then useful to make use of the theorem: A linear mapping of L in $\tilde{L}$ continuous at the origin $a = 0$ of L is continuous in the whole linear space L.

This allows us from this point on to make use of the following definition of continuity for the linear mapping A:

$$a_i \in L \xrightarrow{L} 0 \in L \quad \triangleright \quad A(a_i) \in \tilde{L} \xrightarrow{\tilde{L}} A(0) = 0 \in \tilde{L} . \tag{6}$$

Let L_0 and L be linear spaces and $L_0 \subset L$. Now the set L_0 is said to be 'dense in L' if we are able to find for every element $a \in L$ a series of elements $a_i \in L_0$ that converges in accordance with the convergence in L towards a.

The idea of a dense set serves, as we shall see in § 7, to extend the definition of a continuous functional on the space L_0 to a functional on a space L containing L_0 as a dense subset.

In fact let $A(L_0) \in \tilde{L}_0$ be a continuous functional on L_0, and $a_i \in L_0$ a series converging towards the element $a \in L$ according to the convergence in L. The continuity of A, according to (5), requires that the series $A(a_i)$ tends to a limit if a_i tends to a as its limit. This limit is called then '$A(a)$' by extending the domain of A from L_0 to L.

2. Definition

We move firstly to the definition of a 'convergence in the space $\mathscr{D}$' of a series of indefinitely differentiable functions $\varphi_i \in \mathscr{D}$ with compact support (symbolically: $\varphi_i \xrightarrow{\mathscr{D}} \varphi$).

To this end we require

(1) that the supports K_i of all the functions φ_i are contained in a fixed compact set[1]) $K \subset R_n$;

(2) that these functions φ_i converge uniformly[2]) to a limiting element φ and that, further, all the derivatives of all orders also converge in the same manner:

$$\varphi_i^{(m)} \xrightarrow[\text{unif. } R^n]{} \varphi^{(m)} \quad [m = 0, 1, \ldots] ,$$

where m indicates the mth derivative of φ_i (and $\varphi_i^{(0)}$ being the function φ_i itself).

According to (6) it is possible to define the continuity of a linear functional $T(\varphi)$ of the linear space of functions $\varphi \in \mathscr{D}$ by writing

$$\varphi_i \in \mathscr{D} \xrightarrow{\mathscr{D}} 0 \quad \triangleright \quad T(\varphi_i) \longrightarrow 0 .$$

(Here $T(\varphi_i) \to 0$ designates the usual convergence of complex numbers.)

We are now in a position to give the following definition:

---

[1]) We renounce, by reason of simplicity, to give the most general definition of convergence in $\mathscr{D}$ that would apply to all the possible series $\varphi_i \in \mathscr{D}$.

[2]) The reader should note that the uniformity of the convergence is with respect to the points $X \in R_n$ and not with respect to m.

DEFINITION: By 'distributions' we understand the linear and continous functionals on the space $\mathscr{D}$ of the functions that are of indefinite differentiability and that have compact support.

This is not the most general definition possible. At a later point we shall consider linear continuous functionals of a more general nature, as, for example, on the class $\mathscr{S}$ i.e. of functions that are rapidly decreasing at infinity (cf. § 1). However, it is useful, in developing the fundamental theory, to make use of a simple model of distributions on $\mathscr{D}$.

According to § 1 these distributions build a linear space $\mathscr{D}'$ dual to $\mathscr{D}$ when we define, considering (2),

$$\left.\begin{aligned}
(T_1 + T_2)\,(\varphi) &= T_1(\varphi) + T_2(\varphi) \\[2mm]
(\alpha T)\,(\varphi) & = \alpha T(\varphi)\,.
\end{aligned}\right\} \tag{7}$$

The existence of the functions $\{\varphi(x)\} \in \mathscr{D}$ may not be evident, so we give here an example in one dimension:

$$\varphi(x) = \begin{cases} 0 & [\,|x| > a\,] \\[2mm] \exp\left(-\dfrac{1}{x+a} - \dfrac{1}{a-x}\right) & [\,|x| \leqq a\,]. \end{cases}$$

Now this function is in effect indefinitely differentiable and has compact support $|x| \leqq a$.

We give also at this point some examples of distributions. (1) There exists a class of distributions that may be considered as generalised functions, for we can make them correspond in a unique manner to a function $f(x)$, which is (Lebesgue-)integrable in each compact by putting

$$T(\varphi) = \int_{R_n} \varphi(x)\,f(x)\,\mathrm{d}x \quad [\varphi \in \mathscr{D}]\,.$$

We can show that $T(\varphi)$ is a linear and continuous functional (eq. 5) and hence a distribution. $f(x)$ is called its 'density'.

Conversely the density $f(x)$ of $T(\varphi)$ is determined by $T(\varphi)$ up to a set of points $x \in R_n$ of zero Lebesgue-measure. There is, then, some sense when we write

$$T(\varphi) = \int \varphi(x)\, f(x)\; \mathrm{d}x = {}'f(\varphi)' . \tag{8}$$

We shall have occasion at a later time to use for the functional $f(\varphi)$ of density $f(x)$ the term 'generalised function f'.

(2)   All distributions do not have a density. As an example we might consider the well-known and very simple Dirac measure[1])

$$\delta(\varphi) \overset{\text{def}}{=} \varphi(0) \quad [\text{all}\, \varphi \in \mathscr{D}] , \tag{9}$$

which is a distribution (the linearity and continuity are evident) but not a generalised function, for if we write (9) in density form

$$\varphi(0) = \delta(\varphi) = \int \varphi(x)\, {}'\delta(x)'\; \mathrm{d}x$$

it is easy to see (compare Ch. II, § 2) that the density $\delta(x)$ is not a function in the usual sense although it is written as one and as such is known as the 'Dirac (delta-)function'.

(3)   The Dirac measure is at the heart of a great number of distributions used in physics. Let us begin with the 'transferred Dirac measure' defined by

$$\delta(\overset{0}{\underset{x}{}})(\varphi) \overset{\text{def}}{=} \varphi(\overset{0}{x}) \quad [\varphi \in \mathscr{D}] . \tag{10}$$

If $\delta(\varphi)$ be a 'unit mass' at $x = 0$, then we say that $\delta(\overset{0}{\underset{x}{}})(\varphi)$ represents the same mass at the point $\overset{0}{x}$. For a set of 'masses'

---

[1]) Here we do not make exact use of the definition of the measure. But the Dirac measure is a special distribution such that the expression $\delta(\varphi) = \int \varphi(x)\, \mathrm{d}u(x)$ [u being Heaviside's function (14)] makes sense if we assume that the integral is of a Stieltjes type. This is, however, not the case, in general, for distributions.

$\overset{i}{a}$ at the points $\overset{i}{x}$ we get a measure $\sum_i \overset{i}{a}\delta(\overset{i}{x})(\varphi)$ and for a mass of linear density $\rho(s)$ along a curve $x = u(s)$ in R_n we have the measure $\int \rho(s)\delta_{\{u(s)\}}(\varphi) \, ds$.

By representing in this manner the sources of a field one might treat the case of sources of zero, one, or several dimensions in a coherent and rigorous way in the theory of fields.

(4) Finally let us consider an example of a dipole distribution

$$T(\varphi) = \lim_{\varepsilon \to 0} \frac{\varphi(\varepsilon) - \varphi(0)}{\varepsilon} = \varphi'(0) \,.$$

This example will help in showing the importance of choosing a topology in $\mathscr{D}$. If at the beginning of this section we had defined the convergence as a simple convergence of $\varphi_i(x) \to \varphi(x)$ without any requirement for the derivatives $\varphi_i^{(m)}(x)$, then the linear functional $T(\varphi) = \varphi'(0)$ would not be continuous, for the conclusion $\varphi_i \to 0 \rhd T(\varphi_i) = \varphi_i'(0) \to 0$ would be false.

We might restate here, briefly, the definition of the 'support of a distribution' (§ 1): The complement of the support is the greatest open set $O \subset R_n$ such that $T(\varphi) = 0$ for all functions φ having a support in O.

We say that the distribution T is zero: $T = 0$, if its support is zero. Hence it is possible that the number $T(\varphi)$ be zero (for example if $\varphi(x) \equiv 0$, since by linearity of T $T(\varphi) = T(0 \cdot \varphi) = 0 \cdot T(\varphi) = 0$) without the distribution T being zero.

3. Differentiation

We shall introduce in this and the following sections some operations in the space of distributions $\mathscr{D}'$ (7). To this end we must require that

(i)   the final result of the performed operation shall itself be a distribution;

(ii) in case the distributions reduce to functions, these coincide 'approximately' with the similar operations which are already defined for the functions.

We define now the 'derivative of T with respect to x_k' by

$$\frac{\partial T}{\partial x_k}(\varphi) \overset{\text{def}}{=} T\left(-\frac{\partial \varphi}{\partial x_k}\right). \tag{11}$$

This definition satisfies the conditions (i) and (ii). Verification of (i): it is clear that $T\left(-\partial\varphi/\partial x_k\right)$ is a linear functional having the same dependence on $\left(-\partial\varphi/\partial x_k\right)$ as the form $T(\varphi)$ on φ. Continuity is maintained by reasoning thus:

$$\varphi_i \overset{\mathscr{D}}{\longrightarrow} 0 \quad \triangleright \quad \frac{\partial\varphi_i}{\partial x_k} \overset{\mathscr{D}}{\longrightarrow} 0 \quad \triangleright \quad T\left(-\frac{\partial\varphi_i}{\partial x_k}\right) \longrightarrow 0.$$

In verifying (ii) we shall treat, for simplicity, the case of one variable only. For $T(\varphi) = f(\varphi)$ we must have

$$\frac{\mathrm{d}f}{\mathrm{d}x}(\varphi) = \int_{R_1} \varphi(x)\frac{\mathrm{d}f}{\mathrm{d}x}(x)\,\mathrm{d}x.$$

Indeed by (11) and partial integration we get

$$\frac{\mathrm{d}f}{\mathrm{d}x}(\varphi) = f\left(-\frac{\mathrm{d}\varphi}{\mathrm{d}x}\right) = -\int_{-\infty}^{\infty} f(x)\frac{\mathrm{d}\varphi}{\mathrm{d}x}\,\mathrm{d}x$$

$$= -\left. f(x)\,\varphi(x)\right|_{-\infty}^{\infty} + \int_{-\infty}^{\infty}\frac{\mathrm{d}f}{\mathrm{d}x}(x)\,\varphi(x)\,\mathrm{d}x$$

$$= \int_{-\infty}^{\infty}\frac{\mathrm{d}f}{\mathrm{d}x}(x)\,\varphi(x)\,\mathrm{d}x,$$

φ being zero outside of a compact. (This calculation shows the reason for the minus sign in (11).)

For the higher derivatives the following formula applies[1]):
$D^p T(\varphi) = (-1)^p T(D^p \varphi)$ where the order of the derivation may be interchanged.

We are approaching now the central part of the theory which says that *each distribution is indefinitely differentiable.*(12) This is a consequence of definitions (3) and (11). In particular we notice that each continuous function (and even, each locally integrable function) is indefinitely differentiable.

There exists the converse to this theorem: we give it here without proof:

THEOREM: In a bounded region of R_n each distribution is a derivative to a finite order of a continuous (generalised) function.   (13)

The reason for our introducing the distribution is to be able to differentiate all the continuous functions. This introduction is effected through the aid of a minimum of new elements since, by the converse theorem just mentioned, one obtains nothing else but the derivatives of finite order of the continuous functions.

As a first example let us consider the Heaviside function:

$$u(x) = \begin{cases} 1 & [x \geqq 0] \\ \\ 0 & [x < 0]. \end{cases} \qquad (14)$$

The first and second derivatives are

$$\frac{\mathrm{d}u}{\mathrm{d}x}(\varphi) = u\left(-\frac{\partial \varphi}{\partial x}\right) = -\int\limits_{-\infty}^{\infty} \frac{\mathrm{d}\varphi}{\mathrm{d}x}(x)\, u(x)\, \mathrm{d}x$$

[1]) D^p being a linear form of partial derivation-operators of total order p, e.g. an operator D^2 in two variables:

$$a\frac{\partial^2}{\partial x^2} + b\frac{\partial}{\partial x}\frac{\partial}{\partial y} + c\frac{\partial^2}{\partial y^2}.$$

$$= - \int\limits_{0}^{\infty} \frac{\mathrm{d}\varphi}{\mathrm{d}x} (x) \, \mathrm{d}x = \varphi(0) = \delta(\varphi)$$

$$\frac{\mathrm{d}^2 u}{\mathrm{d}x^2}(\varphi) = \frac{\mathrm{d}\delta}{\mathrm{d}x}(\varphi) = - \delta\left(\frac{\mathrm{d}\varphi}{\mathrm{d}x}\right) = - \frac{\mathrm{d}\varphi}{\mathrm{d}x}(0)$$

thus, by induction, the $(p + 1)$th derivative is

$$u^{(p+1)}(\varphi) = \delta^{(p)}(\varphi) = (-1)^p \varphi^{(p)}(0) \, .$$

As another example: let $f(x)$ be a partially continuous function, $\overset{i}{x}$ its points of discontinuity, $f_i^{(p)} = f^{(p)}(x_i + 0) - f^{(p)}(x_i - 0)$ the jumps of $f^{(p)}(x)$ at $\overset{i}{x}$ and finally $[f^{(p)}] \equiv f^{(p)}$ for $x \neq \overset{i}{x}$ and not defined for $x = \overset{i}{x}$. We get

$$f^{(p)} = [f^{(p)}] + \sum_i f_i^{(p-1)} \delta_{\binom{i}{x}} + \ldots \sum_i f_i \delta_{\binom{i}{x}}^{(p-1)} \; [p = 1, 2, \ldots]$$

which can be proved by induction. We verify it here for $p = 1$ in one variable only: From

$$f(x) = \int\limits_{-\infty}^{x} [f'] (\xi) \, \mathrm{d}\xi + \sum_i f_i^{(0)} u_{\binom{i}{x}}(x)$$

follows

$$f(\varphi) = \int \varphi(x) f(x) \, \mathrm{d}x = \int \varphi(x) \int\limits_{-\infty}^{x} [f'] (\xi) \, \mathrm{d}\xi + \sum_i f_i^{(0)} u_{\binom{i}{x}}(\varphi)$$

and

$$f'(\varphi) = \int \varphi(x) [f'] (x) \, \mathrm{d}x + \sum_i f_i^{(0)} \delta_{\binom{i}{x}}(\varphi) = [f'] (\varphi) + \sum_i f_i^{(0)} \delta_{\binom{i}{x}}(\varphi).$$

Considering condition (ii) we have, cautiously, required that the definition of the operation coincides 'approximately' with the usual definition for the case in which the general definition reduces to special cases. That this is so becomes clear if we consider the case of the derivatives. Indeed the derivative just introduced for the distribution not only generalises that of the functions but it modifies it slightly, for it is well known that the inversion of the order of differentiation of functions is subjected to certain conditions in the usual analysis, whereas in the theory of distributions it is not.

4. Formation of products

In this section we shall define three different products of the distributions T and U, namely

(a)   the multiplication product TU;

(b)   the direct or tensor product $T \otimes U$;

(c)   the composition product $T * U$.

(a)   With regard to the '*multiplication product*', we shall try to define it in such a manner that it is a generalisation of the product $f(x) \cdot g(x)$ in the usual sense, of two functions $f(x)$ and $g(x)$. But we immediately notice that this product does not exist for all distributions, for if $f(\varphi)$ and $g(\varphi)$ be two such distributions defined by the integrable functions $f(x)$ and $g(x)$, $f(x) \cdot g(x)$ is not necessarily integrable and thus does not necessarily define a distribution.

The conditions of existence of the multiplication product are rather complicated and will not be treated here in all their generality. There is a case however in which the multiplication product always exists, namely if one of the factors is the generalisation of a function α that is indefinitely differentiable in the usual sense. This is defined as follows:

$$\alpha T(\varphi) \overset{\text{def}}{=} T(\alpha \varphi)$$

in which the right-hand side is indeed a distribution since

$\varphi \in \mathscr{D} \triangleright \alpha\varphi \in \mathscr{D}$. Furthermore, if $T(\varphi) = f(\varphi)$, this product generalises the usual product $\alpha(x)f(x)$ since

$$\alpha f(\varphi) = f(\alpha\varphi) = \int \alpha(x)\, \varphi(x)\, f(x)\, \mathrm{d}x \,.$$

As an exercise we perform the calculation

$$(\alpha T)'(\varphi) = (\alpha T)(-\varphi') = T(-\alpha\varphi')$$

$$= T\left[-(\alpha\varphi)' + \alpha'\varphi\right]$$

$$= T\left[-(\alpha\varphi)'\right] + T(\alpha'\varphi)$$

$$= T'(\alpha\varphi) + \alpha'T(\varphi)$$

$$= \alpha T'(\varphi) + \alpha'T(\varphi)$$

$$= (\alpha T' + \alpha'T)(\varphi)$$

which may be written in the abbreviated form

$$(\alpha T)' = \alpha T' + \alpha'T \,.$$

We shall also attach some importance to the equation

$$(x\delta')(\varphi) = \delta'(x\varphi) = \delta(-\varphi - x\varphi')$$

$$= -(\varphi + x\varphi')(0) = -\varphi(0) = -\delta(\varphi) \,. \tag{15}$$

(b)   The *direct product* attributes to two distributions, defined for the functions $\varphi(x_1, \ldots x_m) \in \mathscr{D}_x$ with variables $(x_i) \in R_m$ and $\varphi(y_1, \ldots y_n) \in \mathscr{D}_y$ with variables $(y_k) \in R_n$, a third distribution defined for all the functions $\varphi(x_1, \ldots x_m; y_1, \ldots y_n) \in$

$\mathscr{D}_{x,y}$ with variables $(x_i, y_k) \in R_{m+n}$. At this point it would be practical to introduce new and more explicit notation: $T_x[\varphi(x,y)]$ will denote a distribution 'in x' ($\in \mathscr{D}'_x$), namely a continuous and linear functional on the space $\mathscr{D}_x$ of functions $\varphi(x,y)$, where the y's are considered as parameters.

Before giving the definition of the direct product, we give here two theorems of importance for what follows.

THEOREM I: $\varphi(x,y) \in \mathscr{D}_{x,y} \quad \triangleright \quad \varphi(x,y) \in \mathscr{D}_x, \mathscr{D}_y$ where the y and x respectively are considered as parameters.

THEOREM II: $\varphi(x,y) \in \mathscr{D}_{x,y} \quad \triangleright \quad T_x[\varphi(x,y)] \in \mathscr{D}_y$ where the derivative of the function $T_x[\varphi(x,y)] \in \mathscr{D}_y$ is calculated as follows

$$\frac{\mathrm{d}T_x[\varphi(x,y)]}{\mathrm{d}y} = T_x\left[\frac{\partial}{\partial y}\varphi(x,y)\right].$$

(In the case where T is given by an integral one may recognize here a classical rule for the integral of a function dependant on a parameter.)

The 'direct product' is defined by

$$(T \otimes U)_{x,y}[\varphi(x,y)] \overset{\mathrm{def}}{=} T_x[U_y[\varphi(x,y)]]. \tag{16}$$

Let us see first what this means when applied to the case of two functions

$$f_x(\varphi) = \int \varphi(x) f(x)\, \mathrm{d}x\,, \qquad g_y(\varphi) = \int \varphi(y) g(y)\, \mathrm{d}y$$

$$(f \otimes g)_{x,y}[\varphi(x,y)] = f_x[g_y[\varphi(x,y)]]$$

$$= f_x\left[\int \varphi(x,y) g(y)\, \mathrm{d}y\right]$$

$$= \int_{R_m}\int_{R_n} \varphi(x,y) f(x) g(y)\, \mathrm{d}y\, \mathrm{d}x$$

i.e.

$$(f \otimes g)_{x,y} = f(x) g(y)\,.$$

Thus, the 'direct product' eq. (16) corresponds to the usual (direct) product of two functions f and g.

We verify now that eq. (16) does in fact define a distribution for all functions $\varphi(x,y) \in \mathscr{D}_{x,y}$: By theorem I

$$\varphi(x, y) \in \mathscr{D}_{x,y} \quad \triangleright \quad \varphi(x, y) \in \mathscr{D}_y ,$$

x being considered as a parameter. $U_y[\varphi(x,y)]$ can thus be performed and by using theorem II we get $U_y[\varphi(x,y)] \in \mathscr{D}_x$. Thus, the expression $T_x\{U_y[\varphi(x,y)]\}$ always exists. One easily finishes the proof by verifying linearity, which is evident, and continuity:

$$\varphi(x, y) \xrightarrow{\mathscr{D}_{x,y}} 0 \quad \triangleright \quad U_y[\varphi(x, y)] \xrightarrow{\mathscr{D}_x} 0 \quad \triangleright \quad T_x\{U_y[\varphi(x,y)]\} \to 0.$$

The proof that definition (16) is unique is a more delicate one. Let us sketch it: Consider the subset $\tilde{\mathscr{D}}_{x,y} \subset \mathscr{D}_{x,y}$ of all functions which are of the form

$$\varphi(x, y) = \sum_j u_j(x)\, v_j(y) \qquad [u_j(x) \in \mathscr{D}_x , \quad v_j(y) \in \mathscr{D}_y].$$

The direct product of two distributions $T(u_j)$ and $U(v_j)$ can now be calculated explicitly and in a clearly unique manner:

$$(T \otimes U)_{x,y} \Big[\sum_j u_j(x)\, v_j(y) \Big] = T_x \Big\{ U_y \Big[\sum_j u_j(x)\, v_j(y) \Big] \Big\}$$

$$= T_x \Big\{ \sum_j u_j(x)\, U_y[v_j(y)] \Big\} = \sum_j U_y[v_j(y)]\, T_x[u_j(x)].$$

This result can be extended uniquely to the whole of $\mathscr{D}_{x,y}$ by the following three remarks:

(1) $\tilde{\mathscr{D}}_{x,y}$ lies dense in $\mathscr{D}_{x,y}$; [1])
(2) Distributions as linear and continuous functionals are bounded[1]);
(3) A linear and bounded functional defined on a linear space $\tilde{\mathscr{D}}$ dense in $\mathscr{D}$ can always be defined by a unique continuous extension throughout $\mathscr{D}$.

(c) The '*composition product*' of two distributions T and U is defined as follows:

$$(T * U)_z [\varphi(z)] \overset{\text{def}}{=} T_x \{ U_y [\varphi(x + y)] \}$$

$$[\varphi(z) \in \mathscr{D}_z ; \qquad z_i = x_i + y_i ; \qquad x_i, y_i \in R_n \ (\triangleright z_i \in R_n)] . \Bigg\} \tag{17}$$

We note immediately that in spite of the resemblance of the right-hand sides of (16) and (17) there is, however, an essential difference between these two, namely that on the one hand the direct product relates two different vector spaces $\mathscr{D}'_x$ and $\mathscr{D}'_y$ to one product space $\mathscr{D}'_{x,y}$ while the composition product equation establishes a relation between distributions of one and the same space $\mathscr{D}'_x = \mathscr{D}'_y = \mathscr{D}'_z$.

Another difference consists in the following: the composition product does not exist for just any distributions. This follows from the fact that from $\varphi(x + y) \in \mathscr{D}_z [z = x + y]$ it is not possible to conclude that $\varphi(x + y) \in \mathscr{D}_x$ or $\mathscr{D}_y$ (considering y and x respectively as parameters), since the condition under which the sum $z = x + y$ be part of the support of a function of $\mathscr{D}_z$ does not impose any restriction on the individual values of x and y.

We give now a sufficient condition for the existence of the composition product in (17): one of the factors must have a compact support or, more generally, *in a composition product of n factors, $(n - 1)$ distributions must have compact supports.*   (18)

---

[1]) Cp. Riesz and Nagy: 'Functional Analysis'.

Yet this condition is not necessary; in fact for most applications of the theory it is not even fulfilled. There are as many different theories on composition (and often rather elaborate) as there are different sufficient conditions similar to (18). Later on we shall direct our attention to a particular type of distribution, the temperate distribution, which will form the basis of the Fourier theory (§ 7).

To what does the composition product correspond if the distributions are generalised functions? In answering this question it will suffice to limit ourselves to the case of one variable. We have then

$$(f * g)_z [\varphi(z)] = f_x \{ g_y [\varphi(z)] \} = \int\limits_{-\infty}^{\infty} \int\limits_{-\infty}^{\infty} \varphi(z) \, g(y) \, f(z - y) \, dy \, dz \, .$$

i.e.

$$(f * g)_z = \int\limits_{-\infty}^{\infty} f(z - y) \, g(y) \, dy \, .$$

In other words, we get a composition, in the usual sense, of the functions f and g.

We close this section by recalling that the composition, when subject to the condition (18), enjoys such important algebraic properties as associativity and commutativity.

On the other hand there is an example where the composition of say three distributions, in which only one of them has a compact support, exists without being associative. For let $f(\varphi)$ be a distribution defined by the density $f(x) \equiv 1$ (i.e. with non-compact support), $u(\varphi)$ a distribution defined by the Heaviside function (14) (also with non-compact support) and $d\delta(\varphi)/dx$ with compact support (at the origin), then, in anticipation of a result in § 5 and admitting the commutative law for the composition,

$$\left(f * \frac{\mathrm{d}\delta}{\mathrm{d}x} \right) * u = \left(\frac{\mathrm{d}\delta}{\mathrm{d}x} * f \right) * u \overset{(22)}{=} \frac{\mathrm{d}f}{\mathrm{d}x} * u = 0 * u = 0$$

whereas

$$f * \left(\frac{\mathrm{d}\delta}{\mathrm{d}x} * u \right) = f * \frac{\mathrm{d}u}{\mathrm{d}x} = f * \delta \overset{(21)}{=} f \neq 0 .$$

5. Translation and regularisation

We call the 'transfer $\tau_h \varphi(x)$ of a function $\varphi(x) \in \mathscr{D}$' the function

$$\tau_h \varphi(x) \overset{\mathrm{def}}{=} \varphi(x - h) \tag{19}$$

and the 'transfer $\tau_h T(\varphi)$ of a distribution $T(\varphi) \in \mathscr{D}'$' the distribution

$$\tau_h T(\varphi) \overset{\mathrm{def}}{=} T(\tau_{-h} \varphi) .$$

It is clear that $\tau_h \varphi(x) \in \mathscr{D}$ and $\tau_h T(\varphi) \in \mathscr{D}'$.

The definition (10) of the transferred Dirac measure may now be written in the form

$$\delta_{(\mathring{x})}(\varphi) = \varphi(\mathring{x}) = \tau_{-\mathring{x}} \varphi(0) = \delta(\tau_{-\mathring{x}} \varphi) = \tau_{\mathring{x}} \delta(\varphi)$$

from which some important applications would be

$$(\delta_{(h)} * T)_z [\varphi(z)] = (T * \delta_{(h)})_z [\varphi(z)]$$

$$= T_x \{ \delta_{(h)y} [\varphi(z)] \} = T_x [\varphi(x + h)]$$

$$= T_x [\tau_{-h} \varphi(x)] = \tau_h T_x [\varphi(x)] = \tau_h T_z [\varphi(z)] ,$$

i.e.

$$\delta_{(h)} * T = \tau_h T \tag{20}$$

and in particular

$$\delta * T = T . \tag{21}$$

Furthermore,

$$\left(\frac{\partial \delta}{\partial z_k} * T\right)_z [\varphi(z)] = \left(T * \frac{\partial \delta}{\partial z_k}\right) [\varphi(z)] = T_x \left\{ \frac{\partial \delta}{\partial z_k} \bigg|_y [\varphi(x + y)] \right\}$$

$$= T_x \left\{ \delta_y \left[-\frac{\partial \varphi}{\partial z_k} (x + y) \right] \right\} = T_x \left[-\frac{\partial \varphi}{\partial z_k} (x) \right] = \frac{\partial T}{\partial z_k} \bigg|_x [\varphi(x)]$$

$$= \frac{\partial T}{\partial z_k} \bigg|_z [\varphi(z)]$$

i.e.

$$\frac{\partial \delta}{\partial z_k} * T = \frac{\partial T}{\partial z_k}. \tag{22}$$

From the associativity and commutativity of the composition subject to the condition (18) we deduce the rule that the translation and differentiation of a composition product are obtained by transferring and differentiating any one of the factors:

$$\tau_h(T * U) = \delta_{(h)} * (T * U) = (\delta_{(h)} * T) * U = \tau_h T * U .$$

Or, by commuting T and U in $\delta_{(h)} * (T * U)$:

$$\tau_h(T * U) = \tau_h U * T = T * \tau_h U .$$

In the same manner:

$$\frac{\partial}{\partial x_k} (T * U) = \frac{\partial \delta}{\partial x_k} * (T * U) = \left(\frac{\partial \delta}{\partial x_k} * T\right) * U = \frac{\partial T}{\partial x_k} * U$$

and

$$\frac{\partial}{\partial x_k} (T * U) = T * \frac{\partial U}{\partial x_k}.$$

There exists a theorem that says that the composition is the only continuous linear operation changing a distribution into another and commuting with the operation of differentiation.

Let T be any distribution and α a function of indefinite differentiability, further let α have a compact support (in case T has not); then the operation $(T * \alpha)\,(\varphi)$ is called the 'regularisation of T by α'. $T * \alpha$ corresponds itself to an indefinitely differentiable function, called 'reguliser of T'.   (23)

We give an outline of the demonstration by calculating

$$(T * \alpha)_z\,[\varphi(z)] = T_x\,\{\,\alpha_y\,[\varphi(x + y)]\,\} = T_x\,[\int \varphi(x + y)\,\alpha(y)\,\mathrm{d}y]$$

$$= T_x\,[\int \varphi(z)\,\alpha(z - x)\,\mathrm{d}z] = T_x\,\{\,\varphi_z\,[\alpha(z - x)]\,\}$$

$$\overset{1)}{=} \varphi_z\,\{\,T_x\,[\alpha(z - x)]\,\} = \varphi_z\,[\theta(z)]$$

$$= \int \varphi(z)\,\theta(z)\,\mathrm{d}z = \theta_z\,[\varphi(z)]$$

or

$$T * \alpha = \theta \qquad [\theta(z) = T_x\,[\alpha(z - x)]]\,.$$

$\theta(z)$ is indeed a function belonging to $\mathscr{D}_z$ as follows from theorem II, § 4.

Under certain conditions, which we shall consider in the following section, it is possible to discuss the distributions by starting with the properties of their regulisers.

6. Convergence

In the definition of the distribution as continuous functionals, the question of convergence for the series $T(\varphi_i)$ arose. The problem was of a series in the usual numerical space (which may also be complex) and not of a series in the vector space

---

[1]) This point may be verified by integrating $T_x\,\{\,\varphi_z[\alpha(z - x)]\,\}$ as a direct product defined on the subset of $\mathscr{D}_{x,\,z}$ of the functions of the form $\alpha(z - x)$ and by using commutativity of the direct product.

$\mathscr{D}'$ of distributions; for we considered only one fixed distribution in which the arguments φ themselves followed a series in $\mathscr{D}$.

However, it is important to introduce at this point the notion of 'convergence in the space $\mathscr{D}'$' for a series of distributions; the most interesting possibility is the following.

DEFINITION: $T_i \in \mathscr{D}' \xrightarrow{\ \mathscr{D}'\ } 0 \quad \bowtie \quad T_i(\varphi) \to 0.$ \hfill (24)
[For all $\varphi \in \mathscr{D}$ supposed fixed for $i \to \infty$ and uniformly for all so-called 'bounded' subsets $\mathscr{D}_0 \subset \mathscr{D}$ that are formed by all functions whose supports are contained in a fixed compact and that are bounded with all their derivatives.]

The convergence in $\mathscr{D}'$ cannot simply be compared to the usual convergence of functions, the former being weaker than the latter. Indeed we have the theorem

$$f_i(x) \xrightarrow[\substack{\text{uniformly in}\\ \text{every compact } K}]{} f(x) \quad \triangleright \quad f_i(\varphi) \xrightarrow{\ \mathscr{D}'\ } f(\varphi) \ ; \tag{25}$$

but the converse would be false as we shall show by means of an example. First let us state, in relation to the differentiation of distributions, the important fact that the differentiation in the space $\mathscr{D}'$ of distributions is a linear and continuous operation. \hfill (26)

The condition of linearity is none other than a consequence of (11) and (7):

$$\frac{\partial}{\partial x_k}(T + U)(\varphi) = (T + U)\left(-\frac{\partial \varphi}{\partial x_k}\right)$$

$$= T\left(-\frac{\partial \varphi}{\partial x_k}\right) + U\left(-\frac{\partial \delta}{\partial x_k}\right) = \frac{\partial T}{\partial x_k}(\varphi) + \frac{\partial U}{\partial x_k}(\varphi)$$

and the condition of continuity is controlled through the fact that

$$T_i(\varphi) \xrightarrow{\ \mathscr{D}'\ } T(\varphi) \quad [\text{all } \varphi \in \mathscr{D}] \quad \triangleright \quad \frac{\partial T_i}{\partial x_k}(\varphi) \xrightarrow{\ \mathscr{D}'\ } \frac{\partial T}{\partial x_k}(\varphi) \ , \tag{27}$$

an equation that is justified since

$$\frac{\partial T_i}{\partial x_k}(\varphi) = T_i\left(-\frac{\partial \varphi}{\partial x_k}\right), \qquad \frac{\partial T}{\partial x_k}(\varphi) = T\left(-\frac{\partial \varphi}{\partial x_k}\right)$$

and since

$$T_i(\varphi) \xrightarrow{\;\mathscr{D}'\;} T(\varphi) \quad \triangleright \quad T_i\left(-\frac{\partial \varphi}{\partial x_k}\right) \xrightarrow{\;\mathscr{D}'\;} T\left(-\frac{\partial \varphi}{\partial x_k}\right).$$

From (27) we see that a *convergent series of distributions may be differentiated term by term*, for we could as well have written the right-hand side of (27) as follows: $\lim_{i \to \infty} \partial T_i/\partial x_k = \partial/\partial x_k \lim_{i \to \infty} T_i$, which eliminates all doubt with respect to the commutativity of the operation lim and d/dx. We summarize the theorems (11) and (26) in one

THEOREM: *The differentiation of distributions is an always possible, linear and continuous operation in $\mathscr{D}'$.* (28)

According to (8) an integrable function can always be generalised by a distribution. Thus, for all integrable functions the operation of differentiation not only exists but has the nice property of being continuous. Moreover of all possible, generalised function-theories for which (28) holds for, roughly speaking, the class of integrable functions, distribution-theory is, to some extent, the 'smallest' one, i.e. every theory which asserts (28) for all integrable functions must at least contain the space $\mathscr{D}'$ of distributions (cp. theorem p. 11).

In (11) we defined the derivative of a distribution without taking limits in $\mathscr{D}'$; we might have done it by putting

$$\frac{\partial T}{\partial x_k} = \lim_{\Delta x_k \to 0} \frac{\tau_{-\Delta x_k} T - T}{\Delta x_k}$$

for we have

$$\left(\lim_{\Delta x \to 0} \frac{\tau_{-\Delta x} T - T}{\Delta x}\right)(\varphi) = \lim \frac{\tau_{-\Delta x} T(\varphi) - T(\varphi)}{\Delta x}$$

$$= \lim \frac{T(\tau_{\Delta x}\varphi) - T(\varphi)}{\Delta x} = T\left(\lim \frac{\tau_{\Delta x}\varphi(x) - \varphi(x)}{\Delta x}\right)$$

$$= T\left(\lim \frac{\varphi(x - \Delta x) - \varphi(x)}{\Delta x}\right) = T\left(-\frac{\mathrm{d}\varphi}{\mathrm{d}x}\right) = \frac{\mathrm{d}T}{\mathrm{d}x}(\varphi).$$

We show now, by means of an example, that the convergence introduced into $\mathscr{D}'$ by (24) is weaker, for the distributions corresponding to the functions, than the usual one for these functions. We claim that

$$t^\alpha\, \mathrm{e}^{\mathrm{i}tx} \xrightarrow{\ \mathscr{D}'\ } 0 \qquad [\alpha \text{ real parameter}, \quad t \to \infty].$$

Indeed, let n be an integer $> \alpha$, then

$$\frac{1}{t^n} t^\alpha\, \mathrm{e}^{\mathrm{i}tx} \to 0$$

in the usual sense and, in virtue of (25)

$$\frac{1}{t^n} t^\alpha\, \mathrm{e}^{\mathrm{i}tx} \xrightarrow{\ \mathscr{D}'\ } 0$$

whence, because of (27),

$$\frac{\mathrm{d}}{\mathrm{d}x^n}\left(\frac{1}{t^n} t^\alpha\, \mathrm{e}^{\mathrm{i}tx}\right) \xrightarrow{\ \mathscr{D}'\ } 0,$$

but, on the other hand,

$$\frac{\mathrm{d}}{\mathrm{d}x^n}\left(\frac{1}{t^n} t^\alpha\, \mathrm{e}^{\mathrm{i}tx}\right)$$

being proportional to $t^\alpha\, \mathrm{e}^{\mathrm{i}tx}$ it follows $t^\alpha\, \mathrm{e}^{\mathrm{i}tx} \xrightarrow{\ \mathscr{D}'\ } 0$ as $t \to \infty$ although evidently $t^\alpha\, \mathrm{e}^{\mathrm{i}tx}$ is not convergent in the classical sense for $t \to \infty$.

We shall now briefly discuss the question of how to approximate a distribution with the help of functions, as was stated in § 5.

Consider the distributions which are generated by the class of all indefinitely differentiable functions. They form a subclass $\mathscr{D}'_f \subset \mathscr{D}'$, but in addition $\mathscr{D}'_f$ is dense in $\mathscr{D}'$ according to the convergence induced in $\mathscr{D}'$ by definition (24). This theorem, which will not be proved here, allows us to approximate any distribution T as limit of a converging series of indefinitely differentiable functions.

Let $f_n(\varphi)$ be such a series of generalised functions converging towards the distribution δ[1]). We have

$$\rho_n \xrightarrow{\mathscr{D}'} \delta \quad [n \to \infty] \quad \triangleright \quad T * f_n \xrightarrow{\mathscr{D}'} T * \delta = T ,$$

the composition being a continuous operation. T appears as a limit of its regulisers $T * f_n$ which are (by (23)) themselves indefinitely differentiable functions.

7. Fourier transform

The distributions simplify a number of problems in mathematics, owing to theorem (28). As an important example we cite the theory of Fourier transforms. First, let us recall the main relations in the Fourier theory for one variable; the

[1]) Example: The functions

$$\rho_n(x) = \frac{1}{\sqrt{\pi}} n \, e^{-x^2 n^2}$$

$$\rho_n(x) \to 0 \,[x \neq 0] \quad \text{and} \quad \int\limits_{-\infty}^{\infty} f_n(x) \, dx = 1$$

can be shown to satisfy

$$\rho_n(\varphi) \xrightarrow{\mathscr{D}'} \delta .$$

Fourier transform for a function $\varphi(x)$ of the single variable x is given by

$$(\mathscr{F}\varphi)\,(y) = \int\limits_{-\infty}^{\infty} e^{-ixy}\,\varphi(x)\,\mathrm{d}x = \varPhi(y) \qquad (29)$$

in which the existence of this integral is assumed by the sufficient condition that the integral $\int_{-\infty}^{\infty} |\,\varphi(x)\,|\,\mathrm{d}x$ exists. (29) is defined for all real y's. We may build

$$\int\limits_{-y}^{y} e^{ixy} \int\limits_{-\infty}^{\infty} e^{-i\xi y}\varphi(\xi)\,\mathrm{d}\xi\,\mathrm{d}y\;.$$

Then if $\varphi(x)$ is limited in its variation

$$\lim_{|y|\to\infty}\frac{1}{2\pi}\int\limits_{-y}^{y} e^{ixy} \int\limits_{-\infty}^{\infty} e^{-i\xi y}\varphi(\xi)\,\mathrm{d}\xi\,\mathrm{d}y$$

exists and goes over into $\frac{1}{2}[\varphi(x+0) - \varphi(x-0)]$ or, for continuous functions φ, into $\varphi(x)$.

The transformation

$$(\mathscr{F}^{-1}\phi)\,(x) = \lim_{|y|\to\infty}\frac{1}{2\pi}\int\limits_{-y}^{y} e^{ixy}\phi(y)\,\mathrm{d}y \qquad (30)$$

is called the 'inverse Fourier transform'. If

$$\int |\,\varphi_1(x)\,|\,\mathrm{d}x < \infty\;; \qquad\qquad \int |\,\varphi_2(x)\,|\,\mathrm{d}x < \infty$$

$$\int |\,\varphi_1(x)\,|^2\,\mathrm{d}x < \infty\;; \qquad\qquad \int |\,\varphi_2(x)\,|^2\,\mathrm{d}x < \infty$$

it is possible to form the Parseval formula:

$$\int \phi_1(y)\,\phi_2(-y)\,\mathrm{d}y = \int \varphi_1(x)\,\varphi_2(x)\,\mathrm{d}x \qquad (31)$$

$\varPhi_i$ being the transforms (29) of φ_i. Under the same conditions the following relation is shown to be true:

$$\mathscr{F}(\varphi_1 * \varphi_2) = \mathscr{F}\varphi_1 \cdot \mathscr{F}\varphi_2$$

i.e. that the Fourier image of a composition product is equal to the usual product of the images of the factors.

It is clear that this (classical) theory has its inconveniences. The restrictions imposed upon the domains of application have some arbitrariness and some lacking of symmetry with respect to the transforms $\mathscr{F}$ and $\mathscr{F}^{-1}$.

The question therefore arises: can the domain of application be extended to all the distributions in $\mathscr{D}'$, and in particular to all functions $f(x)$ which are generalisable to $f(\varphi) \in \mathscr{D}'$ (7)? Unfortunately this is not the case, as can be seen from the following considerations.

We shall have to introduce the Fourier transform of a distribution as follows:

$$\mathscr{F}T(\varphi) = T(\mathscr{F}\varphi) \tag{32}$$

since this is the only expression that gives a suitable correspondence with the case where $T(\varphi)$ represents a function $f(\varphi)$ which is susceptible to the classical Fourier transform (29). We see immediately that $\mathscr{F}T(\varphi)$ cannot be formed according to (32) when $T \in \mathscr{D}'$, for, $\mathscr{F}\varphi$ does not belong to the domain $\mathscr{D}$ if φ does (because $\mathscr{F}\varphi$ is never of compact support nature if φ is). It follows that a modification of the definition of a distribution as given in § 2 has to be applied in such a manner that to every distribution T its Fourier transform can be built according to (32).

DEFINITION: A 'temperate distribution' is a linear and continuous functional T defined on the linear space $\mathscr{S}$ of rapidly decreasing functions.

The set of temperate distributions form a space $\mathscr{S}'$ which is dual to $\mathscr{S}$. Let us repeat at this point the definition of $\mathscr{S}$ already given in § 1; we have, then, for one variable

$$\varphi(x) \in \mathscr{S} \quad \bowtie \quad \begin{cases} \varphi \text{ indefinitely differentiable} \\[2mm] \lim_{|x| \to \infty} \left| x^k \dfrac{d^m}{dx^m} \varphi(x) \right| = 0 \quad \text{[all } k, m \geq 0\text{]}. \end{cases}$$

We introduce also the 'convergence in $\mathscr{S}$':

DEFINITION:

$$\varphi_i \xrightarrow{\mathscr{S}} 0 \quad \bowtie \quad x^k \frac{d^m}{dx^m} \varphi(x) \xrightarrow[\text{uniformly in } R]{} 0 \quad \text{[all } k, m \geq 0\text{]}.$$

And for the 'convergence in $\mathscr{S}'$' in analogy to (24):

DEFINITION:

$$T_i \in \mathscr{S}' \xrightarrow{\mathscr{S}'} 0 \quad \bowtie \quad T_i(\varphi) \to 0$$

[for all $\varphi \in \mathscr{S}$ assumed fixed while $i \to \infty$ and uniformly for all 'bounded' subsets $\mathscr{S}_0 \subset \mathscr{S}$ (cp. (24)) of functions φ].

Let us examine in more detail the relation between the spaces $\mathscr{S}$ and $\mathscr{D}$ on the one hand and $\mathscr{S}'$ and $\mathscr{D}'$ on the other (see table p. 29).

I: $\mathscr{D} \subset \mathscr{S}$ i.e. $\varphi \in \mathscr{D} \quad \triangleright \quad \varphi \in \mathscr{S}$

indeed

$$\lim_{|x| \to \infty} \left| x^k \frac{d^m}{dx^m} \varphi(x) \right| = 0$$

is always satisfied by the functions $\varphi(x)$ which are of compact support character.

II: $\mathscr{D}$ is dense in $\mathscr{S}$, i.e. that according to § 1, for each element $\varphi \in \mathscr{S} \supset \mathscr{D}$ there exists a series of elements $\varphi_i \in \mathscr{D}$ such that $\varphi_i \in \mathscr{D} \xrightarrow{\mathscr{S}} \varphi \in \mathscr{S}$.

Linear space	Definition of convergence
$\mathscr{D}:$ $\left\{\begin{array}{l} \varphi(x)\text{; indefinitely diff.} \\ \text{compact support} \end{array}\right\}$	$\varphi_i \xrightarrow{\mathscr{D}} 0 \quad \bowtie \quad \dfrac{\mathrm{d}^m}{\mathrm{d}x^m}\,\varphi_i \xrightarrow[\text{uniformly in } R]{} 0$ [all $m \geqslant 0$; all supports of φ_i contained in a fixed compact K]
$\mathscr{S}:$ $\left\{\begin{array}{l} \text{indefinitely diff.} \\ \varphi(x)\text{; } \lim_{\,\lvert x \rvert \to \infty}\left\lvert x^k \dfrac{\mathrm{d}^m}{\mathrm{d}x^m}\,\varphi(x)\right\rvert = 0 \\ \text{[all } k,\, m \geqslant 0] \end{array}\right\}$	$\varphi_i \xrightarrow{\mathscr{S}} 0 \quad \bowtie \quad x^k \dfrac{\mathrm{d}^m}{\mathrm{d}x^m}\,\varphi_i \xrightarrow[\text{uniformly in } R]{} 0$ [all $k,\, m \geqslant 0$; all supports of φ_i contained in a fixed compact K]
$\mathscr{D}':$ $\left\{\begin{array}{l} T(\varphi)\text{; linear and continuous} \\ \text{functional on } \mathscr{D} \end{array}\right\}$	$T_i \xrightarrow{\mathscr{D}'} 0 \quad \bowtie \quad T_i(\varphi) \xrightarrow[\text{uniformly in } \mathscr{D}_0]{} 0$ [$\mathscr{D}_0$: { $\varphi(x)$: bounded with all derivatives and support contained in a fixed compact K }]
$\mathscr{S}':$ $\left\{\begin{array}{l} T(\varphi)\text{; linear and continuous} \\ \text{functional on } \mathscr{S} \end{array}\right\}$	$T_i \xrightarrow{\mathscr{S}'} 0 \quad \bowtie \quad T_i(\varphi) \xrightarrow[\text{uniformly in } \mathscr{S}_0]{} 0$ [$\mathscr{S}_0$: { $\varphi(x)$; bounded with all derivatives and support contained in a fixed compact K }]

III: The convergence in $\mathscr{D}$ is stronger than that in $\mathscr{S}$, i.e.

$$\varphi_i \in \mathscr{D} \xrightarrow{\mathscr{D}} 0 \quad \triangleright \quad \varphi_i \in \mathscr{D} \xrightarrow{\mathscr{S}} 0$$

for we may write

$$\frac{d^m}{dx^m}\varphi_i(x) \to 0 \quad \triangleright \quad x^k \frac{d^m}{dx^m}\varphi_i(x) \to 0$$

all the supports K_i of φ_i being contained in a fixed compact set K.

IV: $\quad \mathscr{S}' \subset \mathscr{D}' \quad$ i.e. $\quad T \in \mathscr{S}' \quad \triangleright \quad T \in \mathscr{D}'$.

In fact if $T \in \mathscr{S}'$, $T(\varphi)$ is then defined for $\varphi \in \mathscr{D}$ according to I; on the other hand the relation of continuity

$$\varphi_i \in \mathscr{D} \xrightarrow{\mathscr{D}} 0 \quad \triangleright \quad \varphi_i \in \mathscr{D} \xrightarrow{\mathscr{S}} 0 \quad \triangleright \quad T(\varphi_i) \longrightarrow 0$$

holds. To identify the distribution $T \in \mathscr{D}'$ thus obtained with the initial distribution $T \in \mathscr{S}'$, it still remains to show that $T \in \mathscr{D}'$ also defines $T \in \mathscr{S}'$ completely.

Now $T \in \mathscr{D}'$ is known for each function $\varphi \in \mathscr{D}$, $\mathscr{D}$ being dense in $\mathscr{S}$ according to II. The functional $T(\varphi) \in \mathscr{D}'$ being continuous in the sense of convergence in $\mathscr{S}$ can then be extended in a one-to-one manner to all the functions $\varphi \in \mathscr{S} \supset \mathscr{D}$ as outlined at the end of § 1, and this extension then coincides with the initially given distribution $T \in \mathscr{S}'$.

Before elaborating the Fourier theory of temperate distributions, we give here some theorems concerning the Fourier transforms (29) in the space $\mathscr{S}$ of rapidly decreasing functions.

THEOREM: The Fourier transform $\mathscr{F}$ establishes an automorphism on $\mathscr{S}$, or symbolically

$$\varphi(x) \in \mathscr{S} \quad \triangleright \quad \Phi(y) = \mathscr{F}\varphi(y) \in \mathscr{S} . \tag{33}$$

Proof:

(a) $\quad \Phi(y) = \int \varphi(x) \, e^{-ixy} \, dx$ exists, since $\varphi(x)$ is rapidly decreasing;

(b) $\Phi(y)$ is indefinitely differentiable, for

$$\frac{\mathrm{d}\Phi(y)}{\mathrm{d}y} = \frac{\mathrm{d}}{\mathrm{d}y} \int_{-\infty}^{\infty} \varphi(x)\, e^{-ixy}\, \mathrm{d}x = -i \int_{-\infty}^{\infty} x\, \varphi(x)\, e^{-ixy}\, \mathrm{d}x$$

(the differentiation and integration were switched, $\int_{-\infty}^{\infty}\varphi(x)\, e^{-ixy}\, \mathrm{d}x$ being convergent uniformly with respect to y).

This integral exists because $x\varphi(x) \in \mathscr{S}$ decreases rapidly towards infinity as well as $\varphi(x)$, since

$$\varphi(x) \in \mathscr{S} \quad \triangleright \quad x\,\varphi(x) \in \mathscr{S}.$$

The successive differentiation may be treated similarly.

(c)   On the other hand a partial integration shows that

$$i y\, \Phi(y) = \int_{-\infty}^{\infty} \frac{\mathrm{d}\varphi(x)}{\mathrm{d}x}\, e^{-ixy}\, \mathrm{d}x\,;$$

this integral exists for any y since

$$\varphi(x) \in \mathscr{S} \quad \triangleright \quad \frac{\mathrm{d}\varphi(x)}{\mathrm{d}x} \in \mathscr{S}$$

and it is bounded. The same holds for any higher order in y say y^k and thus $\Phi(y)$ must be rapidly decreasing towards infinity.

From (33) we conclude (because of symmetry) that

$$\Phi(y) \in \mathscr{S} \quad \triangleright \quad \mathscr{F}^{-1}\Phi(x) = \varphi(x) \in \mathscr{S}, \tag{34}$$

$\mathscr{F}^{-1}\Phi$ being given by (30).

The demonstration of (33) shows not only that the condition $\varphi(x) \in \mathscr{S}$ is sufficient to insure that $\mathscr{F}\varphi \in \mathscr{S}$, but also that it is necessary in the sense that if we postulate indefinite differentiability for the function-class $\mathscr{S}$ (which is fundamental

This theorem rests on the analogous theorem for the space $\mathscr{S}$ (35) by virtue of definition (36) and (37).

The two may be summarized into one, according to which $\mathscr{F}$ and $\mathscr{F}^{-1}$ are linear continuous operations in $\mathscr{S}$ and $\mathscr{S}'$ the continuity being expressed by

$$\varphi_i \overset{\mathscr{S}}{\longrightarrow} \varphi \quad \triangleright \quad \mathscr{F}\varphi_i \overset{\mathscr{S}}{\longrightarrow} \mathscr{F}\varphi \text{ and } T_i \overset{\mathscr{S}'}{\longrightarrow} T \quad \triangleright \quad \mathscr{F}T_i \overset{\mathscr{S}'}{\longrightarrow} \mathscr{F}T \quad (39)$$

which may also be written

$$\mathscr{F}(\lim_{\mathscr{S}} \varphi_i) = \mathscr{F}\varphi = \lim_{\mathscr{S}} \mathscr{F}\varphi_i \text{ and } \mathscr{F}(\lim_{\mathscr{S}'} T_i) = \mathscr{F}T = \lim_{\mathscr{S}'} \mathscr{F}T_i. \quad (40)$$

Hence operations $\mathscr{F}$ (or $\mathscr{F}^{-1}$) and lim are interchangeable and converging series of functions $\varphi_i \in \mathscr{S}$ or of distributions $T_i \in \mathscr{S}'$ may be $\mathscr{F}$- (or $\mathscr{F}^{-1}$-) transformed term by term. In this there are some principle advantages over the classical theory, where in particular (40) is not always valid.

The focal point of the Fourier theory, be it from the theoretical or from the practical point of view, is to be found in the two theorems on composition which we shall state without proof. We give here, first, a lemma necessary to their understanding:

$$T, U \in \mathscr{S}' \quad \triangleright \quad TU \in \mathscr{S}', \quad T * U \in \mathscr{S}'. \quad (41)$$

THEOREM I: $\quad \mathscr{F}(T * U) = \mathscr{F}T \cdot \mathscr{F}U \quad [T, U \in \mathscr{S}'] \quad (42)$

II: $\quad \mathscr{F}(TU) = \mathscr{F}T * \mathscr{F}U \quad [T, U \in \mathscr{S}']. \quad (43)$

The lemmas (33) and (41) ensure that from $T, U \in \mathscr{S}'$ it follows that TU, $T * U$, $\mathscr{F}T$, $\mathscr{F}U$, $\mathscr{F}(TU)$ $\mathscr{F}(T * U)$, $\mathscr{F}T \cdot \mathscr{F}U$, $\mathscr{F}T * \mathscr{F}U \in \mathscr{S}'$.

Examples:

(a) $$(\mathscr{F}\,\delta_{(h)})_y\,[\varphi(y)] = \delta_{(h)x}\,[\mathscr{F}\varphi(x)]$$

$$= \delta_{(h)x}\,[\,\int e^{-ixy}\varphi(y)\,\mathrm{d}y] = \int e^{-ihy}\,\varphi(y)\,\mathrm{d}y\,. \qquad (44)$$

We note that the distribution $\mathscr{F}\delta_{(h)}$ has a density although $\delta_{(h)}$ has not:

$$\mathscr{F}\delta_{(h)}(y) \equiv e^{-ihy}\,.$$

Similarly we get

$$\mathscr{F}^{-1}\delta_{(h)}(y) \equiv e^{ihy} \qquad (45)$$

and, in particular, if $h = 0$:

$$\mathscr{F}\delta(y) \equiv 1 \equiv \mathscr{F}^{-1}\delta(y)\,.$$

(b)   We may solve (44) with respect to $\delta_{(h)}$:

$$\delta_{(h)y}\,[\varphi(y)] = \mathscr{F}^{-1}\,e^{-ihy}\,[\varphi(y)]$$

$$= e^{-ihx}\,[\mathscr{F}^{-1}\,\varphi(x)] = e^{-ihx}\left[\frac{1}{2\pi}\int e^{ixy}\,\varphi(y)\,\mathrm{d}y\right]$$

$$= \frac{1}{2\pi}\iint e^{ix(y-h)}\,\varphi(y)\,\mathrm{d}y\,\mathrm{d}x = \int\left(\frac{1}{2\pi}\int e^{ix(y-h)}\,\mathrm{d}x\right)\varphi(y)\,\mathrm{d}y\,.$$

We obtain thus a (formal) expression for the density 'function' of the distribution $\delta_{(h)}$:

$$\delta_{(h)}(y) \equiv \frac{1}{2\pi}\int e^{ix(y-h)}\,\mathrm{d}x$$

and, for $h = 0$:

$$\delta(y) \equiv \frac{1}{2\pi}\int e^{ixy}\,\mathrm{d}x\,. \qquad (46)$$

(46) is one of the most useful representations of the Dirac δ-function.

(c)
$$\mathscr{F}\,\delta'_y\,[\varphi(y)] = \frac{\mathrm{d}\delta}{\mathrm{d}x}\left[\int e^{-ixy}\varphi(y)\,\mathrm{d}y\right]$$

$$\stackrel{(11)}{=} -\,\delta\left[\int (-\,iy)\,e^{-ixy}\varphi(y)\,\mathrm{d}y\right]$$

$$= -\int (-\,iy)\,\varphi(y)\,\mathrm{d}y\;.$$

We note once more that Fourier transform 'regularises' certain distributions in the sense that they get densities; here

$$\mathscr{F}\,\delta'\,(y) \equiv iy$$

and similarly we arrive at the result

$$\mathscr{F}\,\delta''\,(y) \equiv -\,y^2$$

and in the space R_n of n variables y_i at the result:

$$\mathscr{F}\varDelta\delta(y) \equiv -\sum y_i^2\;.$$

(d)
$$\mathscr{F}\,T' \stackrel{(22)}{=} \mathscr{F}\left(\delta' * T\right) \stackrel{(42)}{=} \left(\mathscr{F}\,\delta'\right)(\mathscr{F}T)$$

(e)
$$\mathscr{F}(\tau_h T) \stackrel{(20)}{=} \mathscr{F}(\delta_{(h)} * T) \stackrel{(42)}{=} (\mathscr{F}\delta_{(h)})\,(\mathscr{F}T)\;.$$

In case $\mathscr{F}T$ has a density $\mathscr{F}T(y)$ (d) and (e) reduce to:

$$\mathscr{F}\,T'\,(y) \equiv iy\mathscr{F}T(y)$$

$$\mathscr{F}(\tau_h T)\,(y) \equiv e^{-ihy}\,\mathscr{F}T(y)\;.$$

The differentiation and the translation of a distribution T are, then, represented in the densities of their Fourier images by a multiplication respectively of a polynomial and an exponential function in y.

In § 8 we shall have recourse to the

THEOREM: The distributions having the origin as support may be represented as linear forms of derivatives of the Dirac measure:

$$T = \sum_{p \leqq m} D_p \delta \qquad [m \text{ a finite number}] \qquad (48)$$

D_p being any operator of differentiation of the order p. In combining with (47) we conclude with the

THEOREM: The density of each Fourier transform of a distribution T having the origin as support is a polynomial in y.

8. Partial differential equations

The aim we have in mind here is not to develop a theory of distributions with application to any particular case, but to give an overall picture which is simple but yet mathematically sound, of the theories themselves. This aim is reached in what concerns the functional theory of distributions (Schwartz) and the question of citing some of the applications, either in mathematics or in physics cannot be done here. So if at this point we give an example, the partial differential equation of elliptic form, our intention is merely to give an idea of the extent of generalisation of the theory (similarly we shall treat only the wave equation in chapter II).

Let $$DT = 0 \qquad [T \in \mathscr{S}'] \qquad (49)$$

be such an elliptic equation, where D is a partial differential operator with constant coefficients, for example up to the second order of differentiation

$$a\,\frac{\partial^2}{\partial x^2} + b\,\frac{\partial^2}{\partial x \partial y} + c\,\frac{\partial^2}{\partial y^2} + d\,\frac{\partial}{\partial x} + e\,\frac{\partial}{\partial y} + f$$

according to (22). (49) may be written according to the linearity of $\mathscr{F}$:

$$\mathrm{D}\delta * T = 0 \quad \triangleright \quad \mathscr{F}(\mathrm{D}\delta * T) = \mathscr{F}\mathrm{D}\delta \cdot \mathscr{F}T = 0\,.$$

$\mathscr{F}\mathrm{D}\delta(y)$ is a polynom in y according to (47); let it be designated by $H(y)$. Now the equation $\mathscr{F}\mathrm{D}\delta \cdot \mathscr{F}T = 0$ only holds if $\mathscr{F}\mathrm{D}\delta$ and $\mathscr{F}T$ have no common support. Thus $\mathscr{F}T$ must have its support contained in the complementary set of the support of $\mathscr{F}\mathrm{D}\delta$, i.e. the set $R_H \subset R_n$ of all y_i's defined by $H(y_i) = 0$. This is a necessary but not sufficient condition, as can be seen from example (15) where we had $x\delta' = -\delta \neq 0$, even though δ' has its support at the origin $x = 0$.

The characteristics of this set R_H give us some indication as to the characteristic of the distribution $\mathscr{F}T$ and then of the solution T.

As illustrations:

(a)   let $R_H = 0$ (nulset) $\quad \triangleright \quad \mathscr{F}T = 0 \overset{(39)}{\triangleright} T = 0$ (50)

there is no solution other than the zero distribution;

(b)   let $R_H = $ origin $\triangleright \mathscr{F}T = \sum \mathrm{D}_p\delta$. It follows from (48) that T is a polynomial in y (47);   (51)

(c)   let R_H be the point $(h_i) \in R_n$. It follows, for instance, that $\mathscr{F}T = \delta_{(h_i)}$ is a possible solution from which we conclude, according to (45), that T is of density:

$$T(y) = \mathscr{F}^{-1}\delta_{(h_i)}(y) = \mathrm{e}^{ihy}\,.$$

Let us, in particular, take a closer look at some differential equations of the second order; of the elliptic type there are 3 special cases:

(a) $$\Delta T - \omega^2 T = 0 \qquad [\omega \text{ real} \neq 0]$$

$\triangleright \quad \Delta\delta * T - \omega^2\delta * T = (\Delta\delta - \omega^2\delta) * T = 0$

$\triangleright \quad [\mathscr{F}(\Delta\delta - \omega^2\delta)](y) \equiv [\mathscr{F}(\Delta\delta) - \mathscr{F}(\omega^2\delta)](y)$

$$\equiv -\sum y_i^2 - \omega^2 \equiv H(y).$$

The equation $H(y) = 0$ has no real solutions, thus $T = 0$ according to (50). Here there are no temperate solutions except the trivial one just given.

(b) $\quad \Delta T = 0 \quad \triangleright \quad \Delta\delta * T = 0 \quad \triangleright \quad \Delta\delta(y) \equiv -\sum y_i^2 \equiv H(y).$

The equation $H(y) = -\sum y_i^2 = 0$ has $y_i = 0$ as a unique root; thus in virtue of (51) there are no temperate solutions except the polynomials called spherical harmonics. If we also require at the same time the solution to be limited in value, then the only possible solution is a constant. This generalises a well-known theorem.

(c) $$\Delta T + \omega^2 T = 0 \qquad [\omega \text{ real} \neq 0]$$

$$\triangleright \quad H(y) \equiv -\sum y_i^2 + \omega^2.$$

$H(y) = 0$ describes a hypersphere. The differential equation has an infinite number of solutions.

All the measures $\mu = \mathscr{F}T$ having their supports over the sphere determine a solution

$$T(y) = \int_{\substack{\text{sphere} \\ H=0}} e^{ixy} \, d\mu(x)$$

which is limited in value.

CHAPTER II

ALGEBRAIC THEORY OF DISTRIBUTIONS

1. Mathematical preliminaries

Here we shall make use of two theorems from algebra. To this purpose let us first define some terms.

(a) The (commutative) 'group' is a non-empty set G of elements with an operation (denoted by $+$) connecting any two of these elements such that

(1) $a, b \in G \quad \triangleright \quad a + b \in G$;

(2) $(a + b) + c = a + (b + c)$ associative law;

(3) every equation $a + x = b$ $[a, b \in G]$ may be solved for $x \in G$;

(4) $a + b = b + a$ commutative law.

If a set G' satisfies only the first two postulates, then it is called a 'semi-group'. A semi-group is said to be 'regular' if

$$a + c = b + c \quad \triangleright \quad a = b \qquad [\text{all } c \in G'] . \qquad (1)$$

In the case of the commutative group we deduce the existence and uniqueness

of a 'neutral or unit element' (denoted '0') defined by $a + 0 = 0 + a = a$ $[\text{all } a \in G]$;

of an inverse element '$- a$' to every element $a \in G$ defined by

$$a + (- a) = (- a) + a = 0 .$$

(b) A 'ring' is a (non-empty) set R of elements with two operations (denoted $+$ and $\cdot$) connecting two elements such that

(1) R is a commutative group with respect to the operation $+$;

(2) $a, b \in R \quad \triangleright \quad a \cdot b \in R;$

(3) $(a \cdot b) \cdot c = a \cdot (b \cdot c);$

(4) $\left. \begin{array}{l} a \cdot (b + c) = a \cdot b + a \cdot c \\ (b + c) \cdot a = b \cdot a + c \cdot a \end{array} \right\}$ distributive laws.

Further R is commutative with respect to $\cdot$ if

(5) $a \cdot b = b \cdot a$

and is said to be 'without a divisor of zero' if

(6) $a \cdot b = 0 \quad \triangleright \quad a = 0$ or $b = 0$.   (2)

(c) A 'field' is a set K defined

(1) like the ring;
(2) with the condition that every equation $a \cdot x = b$, $y \cdot a = b$ [$a,b \in K$; a not being the neutral element with respect to $+$] can be solved for $x,y \in K$.

From this definition we deduce the existence and uniqueness of a neutral element 'e' or '1' defined by

$$a \cdot e = e \cdot a = a \qquad \text{[all } a \in K\text{]}$$

and of an inverse element 'a^{-1}' to a defined by

$$a^{-1} \cdot a = a \cdot a^{-1} = e .$$

Note that a ring does not necessarily contain the unit element e with respect to the 'multiplicative' operation. The set of integer numbers is an example of a commutative ring without divisor of zero but with a unit element e (in this case equal to the number 1). In §2 we shall introduce a ring without unit element.

What we now intend to borrow from the algebra is the following

THEOREM I: Every commutative and regular semi-group H may be embedded in a group G;

THEOREM II: Every commutative ring R without divisor of zero may be embedded in a field K.

The contents of these statements are familiar when we apply them to certain particular cases. For instance the set of natural numbers forms a semi-group with respect to the usual addition of numbers. Theorem I would, in this case, amount to an existence theorem of integers containing the natural numbers. In the same way, the integers form a ring without divisor of zero, with respect to the usual connections $+$ and $\cdot$. The theorem is then none other than the existence theorem of rational numbers.

We prove first theorem II.

Let R be a ring without divisor of zero. We are to find a field K that contains R, $K \supset R$, and which at the same time is the smallest one having this property. This field is known as the 'quotient field'.

To continue let us be guided by the example of construction of rational numbers, starting from the integers. We demand that every equation

$$a \cdot x = b \qquad [a, b \in R; a \neq 0] \tag{3}$$

be solvable ((c) point (2)). x is then determined by a and b and shall be written

$$x = (a, b) \qquad [a \neq 0] . \tag{4}$$

The equality of two such pairs of numbers (a,b) and (c,d) is defined by[1])

$$(a, b) \; '=' \; (c, d) \quad \bowtie \quad ad = bc . \qquad (5)$$

To make sure that this definition is possible, it suffices to verify that what the sign '=' implies is satisfied in accordance with the usual conditions of calculation in equalities, viz. reflexivity, symmetry, and transitivity. And this is the case:

reflexivity: $(a, b) = (a, b)$,   since $ab = ba$

symmetry: $(a, b) = (c, d) \quad \triangleright \quad (c, d) = (a, b)$,

since $ad = bc \quad \triangleright \quad cb = da$

transitivity: $(a, b) = (c, d)$, $(c, d) = (e, f)$

$\triangleright \quad (a, b) = (e, f)$,

since $ad = bc$, $cf = de$

$\triangleright \quad adf = bcf = bde$

$\triangleright \quad daf = dbe \quad \triangleright \quad d(af - be) = 0$

$\triangleright \quad af - be = 0 \quad \triangleright \quad af = be$

because of the condition (2) requiring the absence of a divisor of zero.

We see that definition (5) of the equality is justified in noting that in the well-known case of rational numbers it corresponds to the definition of equality between quotients of integers; we have only to make use of the analogy $(a,b) \sim b/a$ which is naturally imposed on by (3) and (4).

In order to define the operations on the pair (a,b) we start out from the same analogy to rational numbers. We are, then, automatically led to define

$$(a, b) + (c, d) \overset{\text{def}}{=} (ac, bc + ad) \qquad [a, c \neq 0] \qquad (6)$$

---

[1]) ab means $a \cdot b$. We omit the multiplicative connection sign $\cdot$ for simplicity.

for addition and

$$(a, b) (c, d) \overset{\text{def}}{=} (ac, bd) \qquad [a, c \neq 0] \tag{7}$$

for multiplication.

The right-hand sides of these equations exist since

$$a, c \neq 0 \quad \triangleright \quad ac \neq 0 \qquad \text{by (2)}.$$

The only thing is to prove that these operations are compatible with definition (5) of the equality. For it might be that, by starting from different individual pairs chosen in a class of equal pairs in setting up operations (6) and (7), one gets different results. However, this is not the case, as we shall now show.

On the one hand let us add the pairs

$$(a, b) + (c, d) = (ac, bc + ad)$$

and on the other, the pairs

$$(\bar{a}, \bar{b}) + (\bar{c}, \bar{d}) = (\bar{a}\bar{c}, \bar{b}\bar{c} + \bar{a}\bar{d})$$

which are related to the first by the equalities

$$(a, b) = (\bar{a}, \bar{b}), \qquad (c, d) = (\bar{c}, \bar{d}).$$

Can the equality of the sum be proved by starting from the equality of the summands ?

$$(\bar{a}\bar{c}, \bar{b}\bar{c} + \bar{a}\bar{d}) = (\bar{a}b\bar{c}d, \bar{b}b\bar{c}d + \bar{a}b\bar{d}d)$$

$$= (\bar{b}a\bar{d}c, \bar{b}b\bar{d}c + \bar{b}a\bar{d}d) = (ac, bc + ad).$$

In the multiplication case the equality is proved similarly. Multiplication defined by (7) is commutative.

The pairs defined by (3) and (4) form a field. To verify this, it is necessary, according to (c2), to establish the fact that the equation

$$(a, b)\,(x, y) = (x, y)\,(a, b) = (c, d) \qquad [a, b, c \neq 0]$$

is solvable with respect to the pair (x, y). In fact we have only to put

$$(x, y) = (bc, ad) \tag{8}$$

for $$(a, b)\,(bc, ad) = (abc, bad) = (c, d)$$

since $abcd = badc$.

The result (8) is itself compatible with definition (5) of the equality of pairs. The other axioms of the field like the distributive law are easily proved.

We have now to show that the ring R with elements $a, b, c, \ldots$ may be incorporated in the field K of pairs $(a, b), \ldots$ To this end we associate to an element $a \in R$ all the elements

$$(b, ab) \in K \qquad [\text{all } b \neq 0] . \tag{9}$$

This association is a one-to-one correspondence, for, let $b, \bar{b}$ be two unequal elements of R, we have $(\bar{b}, a\bar{b}) = (b, ab)$ since $\bar{b}ab = ab\bar{b}$. Conversely it is impossible to associate the same elements of K with different elements of R, for with $a, \bar{a} \in R$ we get

$$(b, \bar{a}b) = (b, ab) \quad \triangleright \quad bab = \bar{a}bb$$

$$\triangleright \quad bb(a - \bar{a}) = 0$$

and making use of $b \neq 0$:

$$b \neq 0 \quad \triangleright \quad bb \neq 0 \quad \triangleright \quad a = \bar{a} .$$

We get then what is known as a homomorphism of a subset $K' \subset K$ with R. It is defined by the condition (9). It is advisable

to make sure that the association (9) is in fact compatible
with the operations $+$ and $\cdot$ independently defined in R and K.

With regards to the former operation let a, b and $c = a + b \in R$.
If to these we associate respectively (r, ar), $(\bar{r}, b\bar{r})$, $(\bar{\bar{r}}, c\bar{\bar{r}}) \in K$
we find

$$(r, ar) + (\bar{r}, b\bar{r}) = (r\bar{r}, rb\bar{r} + ar\bar{r})$$

$$= (r\bar{r}, r\bar{r}(b + a)) = (r\bar{r}, r\bar{r}c) = (\bar{\bar{r}}, c\bar{\bar{r}})$$

by putting $\bar{\bar{}} = r\bar{r}$.

The compatibility for the multiplication is reached analogously. (9) defines then not only a homomorphism but what
is called an operator-homomorphism between R and $K' \subset K$.
Nothing then prevents us from replacing the pairs in K,
(b, ab), by $a \in R$.

The question now arises if the constructed field is the
smallest satisfying $K \supset R$. The answer is yes. For according
to (4), the field at least contains the pairs (a, b) $[a, b \in R]$.
But our field contains nothing more. In fact as an example
let us consider a pair (a, b) where the components themselves
are the pairs $a = (c, d)$ and $b = (e, f)$, both $\in K$. It is then
possible to reduce (a, b) to a normal pair having as components
elements of R:

$$((c, d), (e, f)) = ((c, dce), (e, fce)) = (de, cf)$$

$$[de, cf \in R] \ .$$

In analogy to the example of rational numbers we shall agree
to write systematically

$$(a, b) = \frac{b}{a} . \tag{10}$$

We can compute with these fractions exactly as is usually
done with the rational numbers in so far as the four fundamental operations $+$, $-$, $\cdot$, $:$ are concerned. This is due to

the fact that the rational numbers form a field. For instance we shall make use of the decomposition in partial fractions in the field of distributions in § 4.

The proof of theorem I is included in that of II. In fact the commutative ring R forms a semi-group with respect to the multiplicative connection. In constructing the field K we automatically incorporated the semi-group in a group, for the field K forms a group with respect to its multiplicative connection. In order to construct such a field K it was necessary to assume the non-existence of divisors of zero such that we might conclude $ac = bc \triangleright a = b$. This is none other than rule (1), used here in the case of a multiplicative group.

2. Definition

As we already mentioned in the introduction there exists at present a large number of different methods of treating differential and integral equations. One of the main postulates for this purpose is to dispose of a 'differentiation theory' (cp. Chap. I, § 3) in which at least all continuous and all stepfunctions are denumerably differentiable. The two examples considered in chapters I and II of this booklet are far from being the only ones. But they are nevertheless characteristic in the sense that in arriving partially at similar results they treat the subject with completely different methods.

Without entering into the details of the correspondence between the two theories it is however worth noting that the algebraic method is more limited than that of Schwartz, as it is unable to treat the distributions with non-compact support character, for example the temperate distribution mentioned in the section on Fourier theory.

On the other hand, however, the algebraic method furnishes us with a direct explanation of the operational calculus as practised for over fifty years in the algebraising of analysis.

(See § 4 where the 'mysterious' calculus of Heaviside will be founded on a quite natural and rigorous basis.) What is more, this method has the advantage of being logically derived from only one guiding idea:

One has to show that the integrable functions of limited support on the left form a ring with respect to the connections of (usual) addition and composition of functions. According to theorem II of § 1 a smallest field contains this ring. The elements of this field will be called 'quotients of composition' (composition-quotients) or distributions[1]).

Let us explain in more detail. We define a class R of functions $\{f(x)\}$ forming a commutative ring, without divisor of zero, with respect to the operations $+$ of addition and of composition $*$ as follows:

$\{f(x)\} \in R$ is a real function of the real variable x for which we have

(a) $f(x) \equiv 0 \quad [x < 0]$
(b) $f(x)$ is integrable, and, more precisely, continuous with the exception of a finite number of discontinuities. $\left.\begin{array}{c} \\ \\ \\ \end{array}\right\}$ (11)

On this function-class an algebraic structure is given by the connections

(a) addition $\quad (f + g)(x) \overset{\text{def}}{=} f(x) + g(x)$

(b) composition $(f * g)(y) \overset{\text{def}}{=} \displaystyle\int_{-\infty}^{\infty} f(y - x) g(x) \, \mathrm{d}x .$ $\left.\begin{array}{c} \\ \\ \\ \end{array}\right\}$ (12)

---

[1]) The idea of composition quotient dates back to Mikusinski. In calling them distributions we follow Erdelyi; it should also be remembered that the latter are not equivalent with the distribution of Schwartz; in fact it seems that Erdelyi himself later decided not to call them distributions (see Operational calculus and generalised functions, Caltech 59).

From (11a) and (12b) we conclude that

$$\int\limits_{-\infty}^{\infty} f(y - x)\, g(x)\, \mathrm{d}x = \int\limits_{0}^{y} f(y - x)\, g(x)\, \mathrm{d}x \; ; \qquad (13)$$

we may pass then from one to the other.

The class R of functions obtained in this manner form in fact a commutative ring without divisor of zero, which can be proved as follows.

First of all we immediately notice that R is a group (§ 1,a) with respect to the addition (12a) in which the neutral element is the function $f(x) \equiv 0$ denoted $\{f(x)\} = f = 0$ as far as elements of R are concerned.

The inverse of the function $f = \{f(x)\}$ is the function $\{-f(x)\}$ (denoted by $-f$). It is then clear that these functions satisfy axioms (11). Axiom (1) of § 1,b is then applicable. It is only left to show that the axions (2) to (6) of § 1,b dealing with the 'multiplication' in R are just equally applicable. Now

(1) is fulfilled as just noted.

(2) from $f, g \in R \quad \triangleright \quad f * g = \{h(y)\}$

$$= \left\{ \int\limits_{-\infty}^{\infty} f(y - x)\, g(x)\, \mathrm{d}x \right\} \in R . \qquad ^{1)}$$

In fact $h(y)$ exists since $f(x), g(x)$ are continuous functions. (11a) is implied by (13) for

$$\int\limits_{0}^{y} f(y - x)\, g(x)\, \mathrm{d}x = 0 \qquad [y \leqq 0]$$

---

[1]) Here the { } are to be understood in set-theoretical sense, i.e. the functions are considered as elements of an algebraic set (R or K). This notation has the advantage, as opposed to the symbols f, g, h, of characterising the variables of the functions used.

since $g(x) = 0$ $[y \leqq x < 0]$.

(11b) is, in all cases, satisfied since $h(y)$ is itself throughout continuous.

(3) $f * (g * h) = (f * g) * h$

proof:
$$f * (g * h) = \left\{ \int\limits_{-\infty}^{\infty} f(y - x) \int\limits_{-\infty}^{\infty} g(x - t) h(t) \, dt \, dx \right\}$$

$$= \left\{ \int\limits_{-\infty}^{\infty} \int\limits_{-\infty}^{\infty} f(y - t) g(t - x) h(x) \, dx \, dt \right\}$$

$$= \{ \iiint f(y - x - t) g(t) h(x) \, dx \, dt \}$$

$$= \{ \iiint f(y - x - t) g(t) \, dt \, h(x) \, dx \} = (f * g) * h .$$

(4) $f * (g + h) = f * g + f * h$

proof:
$$f * (g + h) = \{ \int f(y - x) [g(x) + h(x)] \, dx$$

$$= \{ \int f(y - x) g(x) \, dx \} + \{ \int f(y - x) h(x) \, dx \} = f * g + f * h .$$

(5) $f * g = g * f$.

(6) $f * g = 0 \ \triangleright \ f = 0$ or $g = 0$.

This last point is the most difficult to prove. We shall, in order to render it more intuitive, sketch out a demonstration which, however, is only valid for the subset of those functions $\in R$ with limited support both to the left and right.

The reason for doing this is that there exists for these functions the Fourier transform (I, (29))

$$(\mathscr{F}f) \, (y) \equiv \int\limits_{-\infty}^{\infty} e^{-ixy} f(x) \, dx \equiv \Phi(y)$$

for all finite values of y.

Now in making use of the relations

$$\mathscr{F}(f * g) = \mathscr{F}f \cdot \mathscr{F}g$$

$$\mathscr{F}f = 0 \quad \bowtie \quad f = 0$$

we conclude that

$$f * g = 0 \quad \triangleright \quad \mathscr{F}(f * g) = 0 \quad \triangleright \quad \mathscr{F}f \cdot \mathscr{F}g = 0$$

$$\triangleright \quad \mathscr{F}f = 0 \quad \text{or} \quad \mathscr{F}g = 0$$

$$\triangleright \quad f = 0 \quad \text{or} \quad g = 0 .$$

Thus we conclude that the set R defined by (11) is a commutative ring without divisor of zero. It satisfies theorem II of § 1 and there exists therefore a quotient field K enclosing the ring R.

DEFINITION: Let us call 'distributions' the elements of this field of composition quotients.

In this field all equations $f * \xi = g$ $[f, g \in R]$ are solvable; this (unique) solution being written

$$\xi = \frac{g}{f} \tag{14}$$

according to (10). Here we are to understand that the composition quotients of the functions f, g follow the same rules as the rational numbers.

Finally we achieve this analogy between the functions and numbers by replacing $*$ by $\cdot$, remembering that it is defined by (12b).

We define now the 'multiplicative product $\alpha\xi$ of a complex number α with a distribution $\xi \in K$'.

First of all it is advisable to introduce here the multiplicative product in the ring R of usual functions:

$$\alpha f \overset{\text{def}}{=} \{ \alpha f(x) \} \tag{15}$$

satisfying the rules

$$\alpha(f + g) = \alpha f + \alpha g$$

$$(\alpha + \beta)f = \alpha f + \beta f$$

$$\alpha(\beta f) = (\alpha \beta) f$$

$$1f = f.$$

R forms, then, a linear space (see the definition of a linear space in § 1, chapter I), as long as nothing but the operations of addition and multiplication by a number are considered.

For the distributions (14) the corresponding definition will be

DEFINITION: $$\alpha \xi = \alpha \frac{g}{f} \overset{\text{def}}{=} \frac{\alpha g}{f}. \tag{16}$$

(16) is compatible with definition (5) of equality, for we have[1]) $(a, b) = (c, d)$ or $ad = bc$ every time that $\alpha(a, b) = \alpha(c, d)$ and thus, according to (16), $(a, \alpha b) = (c, \alpha d)$ since $a\alpha d = \alpha bc$ which reduces to $ad = bc$. The theorem is then:

THEOREM: The field of distributions forms a linear space with respect to the addition (12a) and 'numerical' multiplication (16) [2]).

[1]) We make use here of the letters $a, b, \ldots$ instead of $f, g, \ldots$ in order to call the reader's attention to the fact that definition (16) is quite generally possible in any field K and does not depend upon the special 'model' of a field we are concerned with in § 2.

[2]) According to the general algebraic theorem stating that the quotient field forms a linear space, each time the generating ring forms one too (the numerical multiplicative structure of R can be extended to K).

To prove this we have only to compare the axioms of a linear space (§ 1, chapter I) with the help of axioms (12,a) and (16) for the addition and multiplication in K. We restrict ourselves to the proof of 2′ (cp. p. 1)

$$\alpha(a, b) + \alpha(c, d) = (a, \alpha b) + (c, \alpha d)$$

$$= (ac, a\alpha d + \alpha bc) = (ac, \alpha [bc + ad])$$

$$= \alpha(ac, ad + bc) = \alpha [(a, b) + (c, d)] .$$

It is easy to show that K contains elements that are not in R viz. those that are not essentially continuous functions: $\xi \in K \nRightarrow \xi \in R$. To see this more clearly we solve the equation

$$fe = f \qquad [\text{all } f \in R]$$

or

$$\int_0^y f(y - x) e(x) \, dx = f(y)$$

which defines the unit for the multiplication in K. If $e(x)$ were a function $\in R$ we would have had, for $y = 0$:

$$\int_0^0 f(- x) e(x) \, dx = f(0)$$

for all functions $\{f(x)\} \in R$, which is contradictory to definition (11a) since this does not postulate $f(0) = 0$ for all $f \in R$. Thus $\{e(x)\} \notin R$. The ring of integrable functions of limited support to the left is then an example of a ring without unit element with respect to multiplication.

There are different notations in use for this unit $e \in K$:

$$e = 1 = \delta .$$

Some authors also use the functional notation used in (I, § 2):

$$e(x) = \delta(x)$$

where the 'function' $\delta(x)$ is known as the 'Dirac δ-function'.

3. Derivatives and integrals

The differentiation and integration of the distributions $\xi \in K$ are performed with the aid of two operators u and s. u is the Heaviside function: $u = \{u(x)\} \in R$ defined in (I, (14)), and s its inverse

$$s = \frac{1}{u} = \frac{\{\delta(x)\}}{\{u(x)\}} \in K. \tag{17}$$

Composition of any $f \in R$ by u amounts to an indefinite integration:

$$uf = \left\{ \int_0^y u(y - x) f(x) \, \mathrm{d}x \right\} = \left\{ \int_0^y f(x) \, \mathrm{d}x \right\} = If$$

where I denotes the indefinite integral (calculated from $x = 0$). The operation

$$u^2 f = (uu)f = u(uf) = u(If) = I^2 f$$

is to be taken as a double integration and in general $u^n f = I^n f$ an integral of the nth order. We set as the definition of integration of the distribution $\xi \in K$

$$I^n \xi \stackrel{\text{def}}{=} u^n [\xi \in K]. \tag{18}$$

By calculating first u^2, we get

$$u^2 = \left\{ \int_0^x u(x - t) u(t) \, \mathrm{d}t \right\} = \left\{ \int_0^x 1 \cdot 1 \cdot \mathrm{d}t \right\} = \{x\}$$

from this follows, by induction, that

$$u^n = \left\{ \frac{x^{n-1}}{(n-1)!} \right\} = \left\{ \frac{x^{n-1}}{\Gamma(n)} \right\} \qquad [x \geqq 0]. \tag{19}$$

From the associativity of the elements $u \in R \subset K$ follows the associativity of the integration

$$I^m(I^n \zeta) = I^{m+n} \zeta. \tag{20}$$

Because of the conditions mentioned in (18) and (19) we are led to the

DEFINITION of integration to a continuous order:

$$I^\rho \zeta = u^\rho \zeta \qquad \left[u^\rho = \left\{ \frac{x^{\rho-1}}{\Gamma(\rho)} \right\}; x \geqq 0, \rho \geqq 1 \text{ real}, \xi \in K \right]. \tag{21}$$

However, we still have to control the validity (20) of associativity, necessary to a definition of integration, for any real numbers, $\rho, \sigma \geqq 1$:

$$u^\rho \cdot u^\sigma = \left\{ \int_0^x \frac{(x-t)^{\rho-1}}{\Gamma(\rho)} \cdot \frac{t^{\sigma-1}}{\Gamma(\sigma)} \, dt \right\}$$

$$= \left\{ \frac{x^{\rho+\sigma-2}}{\Gamma(\rho)\Gamma(\sigma)} \int_0^x \left(1 - \frac{t}{x}\right)^{\rho-1} \left(\frac{t}{x}\right)^{\sigma-1} \, dt \right\}$$

$$= \left\{ \frac{x^{\rho+\sigma-1}}{\Gamma(\rho)\,\Gamma(\sigma)} \int_0^1 (1-y)^{\rho-1} y^{\sigma-1} \, dy \right\}$$

$$= \left\{ \frac{x^{\rho+\sigma-1}}{\Gamma(\rho)\,\Gamma(\sigma)} B(\rho, \sigma) \right\} = \left\{ \frac{x^{\rho+\sigma-1}}{\Gamma(\rho+\sigma)} \right\} = u^{\rho+\sigma}.$$

Thus we conclude that the functions $u^\rho [\rho \geqq 1]$ build in K a semi-group with respect to the composition of elements which is operator-isomorph to the semi-group of the real numbers $\rho \geqq 1$ with respect to the addition. This isomorphism is determined by the one-to-one mapping

$$u^\rho \to \rho , \qquad u^\sigma \to \sigma \quad \triangleright \quad u^\rho u^\sigma = u^{\rho+\sigma} \to \rho + \sigma .$$

Now, the application of theorem I of § 1 allows us to say that the semi-group of elements $u^\rho \in K$ generates a minimal group G that contains it. It is also clear that $G \subset K$, since K itself forms a group with respect to the composition $\cdot$. In particular every equation

$$u^\rho \xi = u^\sigma \qquad [\rho, \sigma \text{ real}]$$

is solvable:

$$\xi = \frac{u^\sigma}{u^\rho} \in G \subset K \tag{22}$$

in which the definition of equality for fractions is always given by

$$\frac{u^{\sigma_1}}{u^{\rho_1}} = \frac{u^{\sigma_2}}{u^{\rho_2}} \quad \bowtie \quad u^{\rho_1} u^{\sigma_2} = u^{\rho_2} u^{\sigma_1}$$

$$\bowtie \quad u^{\rho_1+\sigma_2} = u^{\rho_2+\sigma_1} \quad \bowtie \quad \rho_1 + \sigma_2 = \rho_2 + \sigma_1$$

$$\bowtie \quad \rho_1 - \sigma_1 = \rho_2 - \sigma_2 .$$

We see that the solutions (22) are one-to-one related only to the difference between the exponents ρ and σ, i.e. one may write

$$\frac{u^\sigma}{u^\rho} = u^{\sigma-\rho} .$$

Care must be taken, however, in ascertaining that this definition is compatible with the case $\sigma - \rho \geqq 1$ where $u^{\sigma-\rho}$

already has a well-determined meaning. The reason is as follows:

$$u^\sigma = \frac{u^\sigma}{u^\rho}\, u^\rho = u^{\sigma-\rho}\, u^\rho = \left\{ \frac{x^{\sigma-\rho-1}}{\Gamma(\sigma-\rho)} \right\} \left\{ \frac{x^{\rho-1}}{\Gamma(\rho)} \right\}$$

$$= \left\{ \int_0^x \frac{(x-t)^{\sigma-\rho-1}}{\Gamma(\sigma-\rho)} \cdot \frac{t^{\rho-1}}{\Gamma(\rho)}\, \mathrm{d}t \right\} = u^\sigma\, .$$

The neutral element of the multiplicative group G is given by the solution of equation $u^\rho \xi = u^\rho$ [ρ any real number] whence

$$\xi = \frac{u^\rho}{u^\rho} = u^{\rho-\rho} = u^0 = 1 = \delta\, .$$

From this we draw the fact that for an inverse operator

$$(u^\rho)^{-1} = \frac{1}{u^\rho} = \frac{u^0}{u^\rho} = u^{0-\rho} = u^{-\rho}\, .$$

Let $f(x)$ be a function the derivative of which exists everywhere. Then, from a classical point of view, we have on the one hand, $\mathrm{D}(If) = f$ where D denotes the operator of differentiation. On the other hand we can calculate

$$f = 1 \cdot f = \left(\frac{1}{u} \cdot u\right) f = (s \cdot u)f = s(uf) = s(If)\, ,$$

hence composition of an arbitrary differentiable function f by the element $s \in K$ amounts to a differentiation:

$$\mathrm{D}^n f = s^n f \qquad [f \text{ differentiable everywhere}]\, . \tag{23}$$

The question now arises whether this definition of differentiation can be extended to all the distributions $\xi \in K$ and, in particular, to all functions $\in R$ of a finite number of discontinuities whose derivatives do not exist everywhere in the classical sense.

Let us consider a function $\{f(x)\} \in R$ with the property

$$\lim_{x<0\to0} f(x) = f(-0) = 0, \qquad \lim_{x>0\to0} f(x) = f(+0) = a$$

and which is differentiable everywhere else. This function has thus as a unique discontinuity a 'jump' a at $x = 0$. Suppose further

$$\lim_{x>0\to0} f'(x) = f'(+0) = 0.$$

Then the function

$$g(x) = f(x) - a\,u(x)$$

is continuous at $x = 0$ and everywhere differentiable and, according to (23)

$$\{\,Dg(x)\,\} = sf - asu = sf - a\delta.$$

But $Df(x)$ coincides with $Dg(x)$ everywhere except at the origin $x = 0$ where a derivative is not defined in the usual sense. It is thus reasonable to generalise the definition of differentiation to the functions with a jump at the origin by the following statement:

$$Df \stackrel{\text{def}}{=} sf - a\delta. \tag{24}$$

The result expressed in (24) may be extended by induction to the case of the nth derivative. Let $\{f(x)\} \in R$ be everywhere differentiable except for $x = 0$; furthermore let us suppose the limits $\lim_{x>0\to0} D^v f(x) = f^{(v)}(+0)$ $(v = 0, 1, 2, \ldots, n-1)$ to exist. Then

$$D^n f = f^{(n)} \stackrel{\text{def}}{=} s^n f - s^{n-1} f(+0) - s^{n-2} f^{(1)}(+0) - \cdots$$
$$- \delta f^{(n-1)}(+0). \tag{25}$$

This relation reduces to (23) for functions which are continuous in all their derivatives up to the order $n - 1$.

In § 4 we shall be concerned with differentiable functions of one variable and a single discontinuity at $x = 0$. (25) will thus hold. But the generalisation of (25) to the case of a finite number of discontinuities is not difficult.

4. Differential and integral equations

The problems of differentiation and integration are reduced by virtue of definitions (21) and (25) to mere algebraic processes in the field K of composition quotients. This surely simplifies the solutions of differential and integral equations. In this section we shall first treat *linear differential equations of one variable containing constant coefficients*. Thus the operational calculus of Heaviside applicable to this class of differential equations appears here in a mathematically coherent form.

A knowledge of expressing all the distributions as functions of the particular distribution s defined by (17) is of the utmost importance in the application of this theory to differential equations. As a beginning let us 'translate' the function $\{e^{bx}\} \in R$ into the language of distributions: One obtains

$$\{(e^{bx})'\} = \{b\,e^{bx}\} \overset{(15)}{=} b\,\{e^{bx}\} = b\delta \cdot \{e^{bx}\}$$

on the one hand, and

$$\{(e^{bx})'\} \overset{(24)}{=} s\,\{e^{bx}\} - 1 \cdot \delta$$

on the other. It follows[1]

$$\{e^{bx}\}(s - b\delta) - \delta = 0 \quad \triangleright \quad \{e^{bx}\} = \frac{\delta}{s - b\delta} = \frac{1}{s - b}. \qquad (26)$$

[1] The expression $1/(s - b)$ is defined by $\delta/(s - b\delta)$; the problem is just a matter of notation.

Using this relation as a basic rule we can derive others, for instance

$$\{ \sin ax \} = \left\{ \frac{e^{iax} - e^{-iax}}{2i} \right\}$$

$$= \frac{1}{2i} \{ e^{iax} \} - \frac{1}{2i} \{ e^{-iax} \}$$

$$= \frac{1}{2i} \left(\frac{1}{s - ia} - \frac{1}{s + ia} \right)$$

$$= \frac{1}{2i} \frac{2ia}{s^2 + a^2} = \frac{a}{s^2 + a^2} . \tag{27}$$

Similarly we obtain

$$\{ \cos ax \} = \frac{s}{s^2 + a^2} . \tag{28}$$

Let us now consider the differential equation with limit condition $y' = by$ $[y(0) = a]$. We look for a differentiable solution for $x > 0$.

$$y' \overset{(25)}{=} sy - y(0)\delta = sy - a\delta = by$$

$$\triangleright \quad sy - b\delta y - a\delta = (s - b\delta)y - a\delta = 0$$

$$\triangleright \quad y = \frac{a\delta}{s - b\delta} = a\delta \{ e^{bx} \} = \{ a\, e^{bx} \}$$

or, in functional form

$$y(x) = a\, e^{bx} .$$

As another example let us consider harmonic oscillations in one dimension as described by the equation $\ddot{x} + kx/m = 0$, a homogeneous linear equation of the second order with constant coefficients, the time t being the independent variable. We have

$$\ddot{x} + \frac{k}{m}x = s^2 x - sx(+0) - \delta\dot{x}(+0) + \frac{k}{m}x = 0$$

$$\triangleright \quad x\left(s^2 + \frac{k}{m}\right) = sx(+0) + \delta\dot{x}(+0)$$

$$\triangleright \quad x = \frac{sx(+0) + \delta\dot{x}(+0)}{s^2 + k/m}$$

$$= \left\{ x(+0)\cos\sqrt{\frac{k}{m}}t + \sqrt{\frac{m}{k}}\dot{x}(+0)\sin\sqrt{\frac{k}{m}}t \right\}$$

according to (27) and (28). The nature of the problem may be such that the initial conditions $x(0)$ and $\dot{x}(0)$ are not known; in this case the unique solution is determined by other factors, say, e.g.

$$x(a) = A , \qquad \dot{x}(b) = B .$$

In this case we make use of the equations

$$x(a) = x(0)\cos\sqrt{\frac{k}{m}}a + \sqrt{\frac{m}{k}}\dot{x}(0)\sin\sqrt{\frac{k}{m}}a = A$$

$$\dot{x}(b) = -x(0)\sqrt{\frac{k}{m}}\sin\sqrt{\frac{k}{m}}b + \dot{x}(0)\cos\sqrt{\frac{k}{m}}b = B$$

in order to calculate for $x(0)$ and $\dot{x}(0)$.

After this example the reader will certainly see that the method is applicable to linear differential equations of any order containing constant coefficients.

Let us consider finally a system of such equations, e.g.

$$\dot{x}(t) + y(t) = \sin 2t$$

$$\dot{y}(t) - x(t) = \cos 2t \,,$$

where the solutions $y(t)$, $x(t)$ satisfying the conditions $x(\pi) = y(0) = 0$ are looked for. A translation in terms of s leads to

$$sx - x(0)\delta + y = \frac{2}{s^2 + 4}$$

$$sy - 0 - x = \frac{s}{s^2 + 4}$$

from which we get x through algebraic calculations in the field K:

$$x = \frac{s^3 x(0) + [1 + 4x(0)]\, s}{(s^2 + 4)\,(s^2 + 1)} \,,$$

and through fractional decomposition

$$x = -\frac{1}{3}\frac{s}{s^2 + 4} + \left(\tfrac{1}{3} + x(0)\right)\frac{s}{s^2 + 1} \,.$$

A retranslation in functions of t according to (28) gives

$$x(t) = -\tfrac{1}{3}\cos 2t + [\tfrac{1}{3} + x(0)]\cos t$$

$$y(t) = \tfrac{1}{3}\sin 2t + [\tfrac{1}{3} + x(0)]\sin t \,.$$

From the condition $x(\pi) = 0$ it follows $x(0) = -\tfrac{2}{3}$ from which we arrive at the definite solutions, viz.

$$x(t) = -\tfrac{1}{3}\cos 2t - \tfrac{1}{3}\cos t$$

$$y(t) = \tfrac{1}{3}\sin 2t - \tfrac{1}{3}\sin t \,.$$

Hence the method to be used in solving a system of linear differential equations with constant coefficients (in one variable but of any order) may be summarised as follows:

(a)   express the derivatives of the unknown functions as well as other functions of R that eventually appear in the system in terms of the distribution $s \in K$ making use of definition (25) for the derivatives and of the formulae (26), (27) and (28) (and similar) for those other functions.

(b)   solve the system algebraically with respect to the unknown functions (distributions) using as a basis the isomorphism of the field K of distributions with the field of the rational numbers. (All the rules of calculation valid in the latter are also valid in K. Take as an example the method of decomposition in fractions as used in the last example.)

(c)   re-interpret the solutions, if possible[1]), as functions $\in R$ with the aid of formulas of the type (26), (27), (28).

(d)   investigate the initial conditions as in the usual analysis.

On the other hand an algebra-like translation of *integral equations of compositional type* can be attained with the aid of the distributions; e.g. let us consider the following linear equations

$$\int_0^x k(x - t)\, y(t)\, \mathrm{d}t = f(x) \tag{29}$$

$$\int_0^x k(x - t)\, y(t)\, \mathrm{d}t - y(x) = f(x)\,, \tag{30}$$

where $y(x)$ is the unknown function. The left-hand sides can

----

[1]) A system of differential equations does not necessarily have its solutions as functions in the ring R.

be taken as compositions of the functions k and y if we assume them to be elements of R.[1])

We solve now (29) for the case where the kernel k is defined by

$$k(x - t) = (x - t)^{-\lambda} \qquad [0 < \lambda < 1]$$

or, expressed as an element of K, according to (21) and remembering that in the integral $x - t \geq 0$:

$$k = \{ (x - t)^{-\lambda} \} = \Gamma(1 - \lambda)\, u^{1-\lambda}$$

$\Gamma(1 - \lambda)$ exists, since $1 - \lambda > 0$; hence in K, (29) corresponds to equation $ky = \Gamma(1 - \lambda)u^{1-\lambda}y = f$ and consequently

$$y = \frac{f u^{\lambda-1}}{\Gamma(1 - \lambda)}.$$

This expression cannot be directly translated to a function of R since in $u^{\lambda-1}$, $\lambda - 1$ is negative. Therefore let us build

$$Iy = uy = \frac{f u^{\lambda}}{\Gamma(1 - \lambda)} = \frac{f}{\Gamma(1 - \lambda)} \left\{ \frac{x^{\lambda-1}}{\Gamma(\lambda)} \right\}$$

$$= \frac{1}{\Gamma(1 - \lambda)\Gamma(\lambda)} f \{ x^{\lambda-1} \}$$

$$= \frac{\sin(\pi\lambda)}{\pi} \left\{ \int_{0}^{x} (x - t)^{\lambda-1} f(t)\, dt \right\},$$

---

[1]) From the theory of integral equations these two equations belong to a subclass of equations known as the Volterra integral equations of the first and second kind respectively. They are defined in the same way as (29) and (30) except that the kernel is more generalised.

and then differentiate in order to obtain the solution

$$y = \frac{\sin (\pi\lambda)}{\pi} \left\{ \frac{d}{dx} \int_0^x (x - t)^{\lambda - 1} f(t) \, dt \right\}$$

or still as a function

$$y(x) = \frac{\sin (\pi\lambda)}{\pi} \frac{d}{dx} \int_0^x (x - t)^{\lambda - 1} f(t) \, dt .$$

The solution of the second equation (30) will be obtained in a way analogous if not easier. As an illustration let us take the special case

$$\int_0^x \sin (x - t) \, y(t) \, dt - y(x) = ax$$

or, in K:

$$\frac{y}{s^2 + 1} - y = \{ ax \} = \frac{a}{s^2}$$

whence

$$y = \frac{a}{s^2} + \frac{a}{s^4} = a \{ x \} + a \left\{ \frac{x^3}{6} \right\}$$

or, as a function

$$y(x) = ax + a \frac{x^3}{6} .$$

As a last case, we may call to the reader's attention the case of *integro-differential* equations of the type

$$\int_0^x k(x - t) \, y'(t) \, dt - y(x) = f(x)$$

which may be treated in a similar way.

5. Relation to the Laplace transform

The differential and integral equations that we have considered up to now may also be treated with a Laplace transform. Although this method is more complicated, mathematically speaking, than that which we have developed up to now, since its use necessitates a meticulous study of analytical functions, it is interesting to verify the isomorphism existing between the algebra of functions as elements of the field K of distributions and the algebra of the Laplace transforms of these functions.

First of all let us give the

DEFINITION of the 'Laplace transform of a continuous function'

$$(\mathscr{L}f)(s) = \int_0^\infty e^{-sx} f(x)\, dx = \bar{f}(s) \qquad [s \text{ complex}]$$

and of its inverse[1])

$$(\mathscr{L}^{-1}\bar{f})(x) = \frac{1}{2\pi} \int_{-\infty}^\infty e^{x(\xi + i\eta)} \bar{f}(\xi + i\eta)\, d\eta = f(x) \qquad [\xi > 0].$$

From this we can move to a sketchy proof of the above-mentioned isomorphism, as follows:

(a) To the composition of two functions $f, g \in R$ corresponds the usual multiplication of their Laplace transforms

$$\mathscr{L}(f * g) = \mathscr{L}f \cdot \mathscr{L}g.$$

Proof:

$$\int_0^\infty e^{-sy} \int_0^y f(y - x) g(x)\, dx\, dy = \int_0^\infty e^{-s\xi} f(\xi)\, d\xi \int_0^\infty e^{-sx} g(x)\, dx$$

---

[1]) The conditions of existence for the inverse falls back on a detailed study of complex functions; this would complicate the here given formulae. By staying within algebraic bounds our reasoning remains simple enough.

if we substitute $\xi + x$ for y and remember (11a).

(b) The Laplace transform of the Heaviside function $u(x)$ is

$$(\mathscr{L}u)(s) = 1/s.$$

Proof:

$$\int_0^\infty e^{-sx} u(x) \, dx = \int_0^\infty e^{-sx} \, dx = \frac{1}{s}.$$

(c) $(\mathscr{L}\{e^{ax}\})(s) = \dfrac{1}{s-a}.$

Proof:

$$\int_0^\infty e^{-sx} e^{ax} \, dx = \frac{1}{s-a}.$$

(d) $(\mathscr{L}\{\sin ax\})(s) = \dfrac{a}{s^2 + a^2}$; $(\mathscr{L}\{\cos ax\})(s) = \dfrac{s}{s^2 + a^2}.$

Proof: we have only to use the fact that the Laplace transform $\mathscr{L}$ is a linear operation in f, for then

$$(\mathscr{L}\{\sin ax\})(s) = \left(\mathscr{L}\left\{ \frac{e^{iax} - e^{-iax}}{2i} \right\} \right)(s)$$

$$= \frac{1}{2i} [(\mathscr{L}\{e^{iax}\})(s) - (\mathscr{L}\{e^{-iax}\})(s)]$$

$$= \frac{1}{2i} \left(\frac{1}{s - ia} - \frac{1}{s + ia} \right) = \frac{s}{s^2 + a^2}$$

and similarly for the case of $\mathscr{L}\{\cos ax\}$.

(e) $(\mathscr{L}f')(s) = s(\mathscr{L}f)(s) - f(0).$

Proof:

$$\int_0^\infty e^{-sx} f'(x) \, dx = f(x) e^{-sx} \Big|_0^\infty + s \int_0^\infty e^{-sx} f(x) \, dx = -f(0) + s(\mathscr{L}f)(s).$$

(f) $(\mathscr{L}If)\,(s) = \dfrac{1}{s}\,(\mathscr{L}f)\,(s) = (\mathscr{L}u)\,(s)\cdot(\mathscr{L}f)\,(s) = (\mathscr{L}(u * f))\,(s)$.

Proof:

$$\int\limits_{0}^{\infty} e^{-sx} \int\limits_{0}^{x} f(\xi)\,\mathrm{d}\xi\,\mathrm{d}x = \left. -\frac{1}{s}\,e^{-sx} \int\limits_{0}^{x} f(\xi)\,\mathrm{d}\xi\,\right|_{0}^{\infty} + \frac{1}{s}\int\limits_{0}^{\infty} e^{-sx} f(x)\,\mathrm{d}x$$

$$= \frac{1}{s}\,(\mathscr{L}f)\,(s) \ .$$

We note that the rules (a) to (f) for the Laplace transforms of the functions f correspond respectively to the rules (12b), (17), (26), (27/28), (24), (18), valid for the distributions corresponding to the same functions. From (e) and (f) we may easily derive, by induction, the formulae for $\mathscr{L}D^n f$ and $\mathscr{L}I^n f$ that are similar to (25) and (18).

Starting from these rules we may then translate 'word for word' the solutions of the differential and integral equations treated in § 4 into the 'language' of the Laplace transform.

However, there exist in the Laplace theory certain rules for which we have not established analogies in the distribution theory. Of these we shall mention only one that allows us to find the Laplace images of the linear differential equations with non-constant coefficients. Namely:

$$(\mathscr{L}\,\{\,x\,f(x)\,\}\,)\,(s) = -\frac{\mathrm{d}}{\mathrm{d}s}\,(\mathscr{L}f)\,(s)$$

for which the proof is immediate:

$$\int\limits_{0}^{\infty} e^{-sx}\,x\,f(x)\,\mathrm{d}x = -\frac{\mathrm{d}}{\mathrm{d}s}\int\limits_{0}^{\infty} e^{-sx} f(x)\,\mathrm{d}x \ .$$

Consider now the linear differential equation of 2nd order in x:

$$xy'' - y' - xy = 0 \ .$$

Its Laplace image is

$$(\mathscr{L}\{xy''\})(s) = -\frac{\mathrm{d}}{\mathrm{d}s}(\mathscr{L}y'')(s) = -\frac{\mathrm{d}}{\mathrm{d}s}[s^2(\mathscr{L}y)(s) - y'(0) - sy(0)]$$

$$(\mathscr{L}y)(s) = s(\mathscr{L}y)(s) - y(0)$$

$$(\mathscr{L}\{xy\})(s) = -\frac{\mathrm{d}}{\mathrm{d}s}(\mathscr{L}y)(s)$$

$$\rhd \quad (s^2 - 1)\frac{\mathrm{d}}{\mathrm{d}s}(\mathscr{L}y)(s) + 3s(\mathscr{L}y)(s) - 2y(0) = 0,$$

i.e. a linear differential equation of the 1st order with variable coefficients, the solution of which is well known in classical analysis. This solution should, of course, be retransformed by the operation $\mathscr{L}^{-1}$ in order to give the solution of the original problem. This method is useful each time the coefficients are lower order polynomials in x than the order of the differential equation in question, for it reduces the latter.

The translation of this procedure into the theory of distributions requires the introduction of a differentiation in K with respect to the distribution s. This has not been done yet.

6. Convergence

It is surprising to see the results that are obtained when treating distributions from a purely algebraic point of view. None the less, when we go further and would like to make some applications, for example, to the partial differential equations, we shall have to use an *analysis of distribution*. To this end we shall introduce such ideas as 'continuous functions' or 'differentiable functions' of a distribution. First and foremost, a definition of the convergence in the field K of the distributions must be given.

We start with the 'convergence in R' of the functions $f_n(x) \in R$ (denoted by $\xrightarrow{R}$):

DEFINITION:

$$f_n(x) \in R \xrightarrow{R} f(x) \in R$$

⋈   to all $\varepsilon, x_0 > 0$ there exists

a number $N(\varepsilon, x_0)$ such that

$$|f_n(x) - f(x)| < \varepsilon \qquad [n > N]$$

uniformly for all x $[0 \leq x \leq x_0]$.   (31)

The 'convergence in K' of the distributions $\xi_n \in K$ (denoted $\xrightarrow{K}$) is then given by the

DEFINITION:

$$\xi_n \in K \xrightarrow{K} \xi \in K$$

⋈   there exists an element $q \in R$ such that $q\xi_n, q\xi$ are functions
in R (for all n) and $q\xi_n \xrightarrow{R} q\xi$.   (32)

The convergence in K is less strong than that in R. Thus the function (already considered in I, § 6 in the same context)

$$f(x) = \begin{cases} 0 & [x < 0] \\ t^\alpha e^{itx} & [x \geq 0; \alpha \text{ real} \geq 0] \end{cases}$$

does not converge towards 0 for $t \to \infty$ in the usual sense of (31); whereas $\{f(x)\} \in K$ when considered as a distribution converges according to (32). Let us show this in the simple case $\alpha = 0$ where we may choose $q = \{u(x)\}$:

$$\{u(x)\}\{e^{itx}\} = \left\{ \int_0^y e^{itx} \, dx \right\} = \left\{ \frac{1}{it} e^{itx} \Big|_0^y \right\}$$

$$= \left\{ \frac{1}{it}\left(e^{ity} - 1\right) \right\} \xrightarrow{R} 0 = \{u(x)\}\{0\}.$$

In the case of an arbitrary real $\alpha > 0$ we would have to make use of $q = u^\beta$ [$\beta > \alpha$] in (32).

The convergence in K allows us therefore (as in $\mathscr{D}'$ for the case of Schwartz' distributions), to attribute a limit to a series of functions which otherwise would be divergent.

Among the applications of the convergence in K we find the particularly interesting formula

$$\left\{ \frac{nf(nx)}{\displaystyle\int_0^\infty f(t)\,dt} \right\} \xrightarrow{K} \delta \tag{33}$$

in which $\int_0^\infty |f(t)|\,dt$ of course is assumed to exist.

This formula determines as is well known a class of functions $\{\delta_n(x)\}$ approximating the Dirac 'function' δ. By putting

(a)　$f(x) = \dfrac{1}{1 + x^2}$　we would have　$\delta_n(x) = \dfrac{2}{\pi}\dfrac{n}{1 + n^2 x^2}$

and by putting

(b)　$f(x) = e^{-x^2}$　we would have　$\delta_n(x) = \dfrac{1}{\sqrt{\pi}} n\, e^{-n^2 x^2}$.

The proof to (33) is given by showing that

$$u^2 \left\{ \frac{nf(nx)}{\displaystyle\int_0^\infty f(t)\,dt} \right\}$$

corresponds to a function of R and converges as such in R towards the function $u^2 \delta = \{\,x\,\}$. u^2 there plays the role of q in the definition (32).

Let us imagine the distribution $\xi \in K$ to be functions of a set $\lambda, \mu, \nu, \ldots$ of continuous real variables, of which, for the sake of simplicity, we shall limit ourselves to only one variable λ; all the results may be extended without much effort to the case of a finite number of variables.

A function $\xi(\lambda)$ of distributions is said to be 'continuous at the point λ' if we know that for all the series $\lambda_n \to \lambda$ of arguments $\xi(\lambda_n) \xrightarrow{K} \xi(\lambda)$.

The differentiation and integration with respect to λ are defined at first for the class $\mathscr{C}$ of functions $a(\lambda, x)$ which are differentiable and integrable with respect to λ and are $\in R$ in their dependence on x for each fixed λ:

$$a'(\lambda) \stackrel{\text{def}}{=} \left\{ \frac{\partial a(\lambda, x)}{\partial \lambda} \right\} \tag{34}$$

$$\int_{\lambda_1}^{\lambda_2} a(\lambda) \, d\lambda \stackrel{\text{def}}{=} \left\{ \int_{\lambda_1}^{\lambda_2} a(\lambda, x) \, d\lambda \right\}. \tag{35}$$

This being done one can introduce differentiation and integration for all functions of distributions $\xi(\lambda)$ which satisfy the following condition: There exists a $q \in R$ such that $(q\xi(\lambda))'$ and $\int_{\lambda_1}^{\lambda_2} q\xi(\lambda) \, d\lambda$ exist, i.e. such that $q\xi(\lambda) \in \mathscr{C}$ and $\in R$ in its dependence on x. Differentiation and integration of ξ are then defined as follows:

$$\xi'(\lambda) \stackrel{\text{def}}{=} q^{-1}(q\xi(\lambda))' \tag{36}$$

$$\int_{\lambda_1}^{\lambda_2} \xi(\lambda) \, d\lambda \stackrel{\text{def}}{=} q^{-1} \int_{\lambda_1}^{\lambda_2} q\xi(\lambda) \, d\lambda. \tag{37}$$

We still have to show that the definitions (36) and (37) are independent of the function $q \in R$ chosen. For the case of differentiation the equation $(q\xi(\lambda))' = q\xi'(\lambda)$ is used, $q \in R$ being a function independent of λ. We suppose that the usual derivatives $(q_i \xi(\lambda))'$ as given by (34) exist for the two functions $q_i \in R$ $(i = 1, 2)$, this condition being necessary in (36). We have then

$$q_1^{-1} (q_1 \xi(\lambda))' = q_1^{-1} q_2^{-1} q_2 (q_1 \xi(\lambda)'$$

$$= q_1^{-1} q_2^{-1} q_1 (q_2 \xi(\lambda))' = q_2^{-1} (q_2 \xi(\lambda))' .$$

The proof is similar for the integration. One easily verifies compatibility of definitions (34) to (37) in the case $\xi(\lambda)$ is a differentiable or integrable function with respect to λ. Higher order derivatives and integrals may be defined analogously.

7. Translation and the exponential function[1])

We define a function

$$h_a(\lambda, x) \overset{\text{def}}{=} \begin{cases} 0 & [0 \leqq x < \lambda] \\[2ex] \dfrac{(x - \lambda)^{a-1}}{\Gamma(a)} & [\lambda \leqq x < \infty \,; \operatorname{Re} a > 0] \end{cases} \tag{38}$$

which we may write as a one-variable function of distributions:

$$h_a(\lambda) = \{ h_a(\lambda, x) \} .$$

For $a = 1$ we obtain in particular

$$h_1(\lambda, x) = u(x - \lambda) \,; \qquad h_1(0, x) = u(x)$$

$u(x)$ being the Heaviside function defined in chapter I. Furthermore we get

$$u^a h_1(\lambda) = h_{a+1}(\lambda) \qquad [\operatorname{Re} a > 0] \tag{39}$$

[1]) This section cannot be easily extended to include more variables. It is a preparation for the 2-dimensional application of § 8.

for

$$u^a h_1(\lambda) = u^a \{ u(x - \lambda) \} = \left\{ \int_0^y u^a(y - x) \, u(x - \lambda) \, \mathrm{d}x \right\}$$

$$= \left\{ \int_0^{y-\lambda} u^a(y - \bar{x} - \lambda) \, u(\bar{x}) \, \mathrm{d}\bar{x} \right\}$$

$$= \left\{ \int_0^{\bar{y}} u^a(\bar{y} - \bar{x}) \, u(\bar{x}) \, \mathrm{d}\bar{x} \right\} = \{ u^{a+1} \, (\bar{y}) \}$$

$$= \begin{cases} 0 & [\bar{y} < 0] \\ \dfrac{\bar{y}^a}{\Gamma(a+1)} & [\bar{y} \geqq 0] \end{cases} = \begin{cases} 0 & [y < \lambda] \\ \dfrac{(y - \lambda)^a}{\Gamma(a+1)} & [y \geqq \lambda] \end{cases}.$$

Furthermore

$$h_1(\lambda) \, h_1(\mu) = u h_1(\lambda + \mu) = h_2(\lambda + \mu) \tag{40}$$

for

$$\left\{ \int_0^y h_1(\lambda, y - x) \, h_1(\mu, x) \, \mathrm{d}x \right\} = \left\{ \int_\mu^{y-\lambda} u(y - x - \lambda) \, u(x - \mu) \, \mathrm{d}x \right\}$$

$$= \left\{ \int_0^{\bar{y}} u(\bar{y} - \bar{x}) \, u(\bar{x}) \, \mathrm{d}\bar{x} \right\} = \{ \bar{y} \} = \{ y - \lambda - \mu \}$$

$$= h_2(\lambda + \mu).$$

The rule (39) allows us to generalise the definition (38) to negative indices:

$$h_{-a+1}(\lambda) \overset{\text{def}}{=} u^{-a} h_1(\lambda) = s^a h_1(\lambda) \qquad [a > 0] \tag{41}$$

and it follows, from (40), by multiplying with s^2:

$$h_0(\lambda)\, h_0(\mu) = h_0(\lambda + \mu)\,. \tag{42}$$

Equation (40) permits us to define $h(\lambda)$ when λ is negative:

$$h_1(\lambda)h_1(a - \lambda) = uh_1(a)$$

$$\triangleright \quad h_1(\lambda)h_1(-\lambda) = uh_1(0)$$

$$\triangleright \quad h_1(-\lambda) = \frac{uh_1(0)}{h_1(\lambda)} = \frac{u^2}{h_1(\lambda)}\,. \tag{43}$$

Combining (41) and (43):

$$h_0(-\lambda) = sh_1(-\lambda) = \frac{u^2 s}{h_1(\lambda)} = \frac{u}{h_1(\lambda)} = \frac{1}{sh_1(\lambda)} = \frac{1}{h_0(\lambda)}\,.$$

We note finally that the composition of the function $f(x)$ with $h_0(\lambda)$ leads to a translation τ_λ of the function $f(x)$ to the function $f(x - \lambda)$ (I, § 5) for we have

$$h_0(\lambda)\,\{\,f(x)\,\} = sh_1(\lambda)\,\{\,f(x)\,\} = s\left\{ \int\limits_0^{y-\lambda} f(x)\,\mathrm{d}x \right\}$$

$$= \left\{ \begin{array}{ll} f(y - \lambda) & [\lambda \leqq y < \infty] \\ 0 & [0 \leqq y < \lambda] \end{array} \right\} = \tau_\lambda f\,. \tag{44}$$

Hence $h_0(\lambda)$ plays the role of a translation operator τ_λ.

The distributions $h_a(\lambda)$ are for each a differentiable and integrable functions in λ according to (36) and (37). We shall prove this for $h_1(\lambda)$ and $h_0(\lambda)$ and for the case of the differentiation only:

$$h_1'(\lambda) = s^2 \, [u^2 h_1(\lambda)]' = s^2 \, [h_3(\lambda)]'$$

$$= s^2 \left\{ \begin{array}{ll} 0 & [x < \lambda] \\ \dfrac{\mathrm{d}}{\mathrm{d}\lambda}\left(\dfrac{(x-\lambda)^2}{\Gamma(3)}\right) & [x \geqq \lambda] \end{array} \right\} = s^2 \left\{ \begin{array}{ll} 0 & [x < \lambda] \\ -(x-\lambda) & [x \geqq \lambda] \end{array} \right\}$$

$$= -s^2 h_2(\lambda) = -h_0(\lambda)$$

in which u^2 here plays the role of the element $q \in R$ in (36) such that $u^2 h_1(\lambda) = h_3(\lambda)$ becomes differentiable in the sense of (34). For the case of $h_0(\lambda)$ we choose $q = u^3$:

$$h_0'(\lambda) = s^3 \, [u^3 h_0(\lambda)]' = s^3 \, [h_3(\lambda)]'$$

$$= s^3 \, [- h_2(\lambda)] = - h_{-1}(\lambda) . \qquad (45)$$

We calculate now an expression that will be useful to us in the applications:[1])

$$\int\limits_0^\infty h_0(\lambda)\, f(\lambda)\, \mathrm{d}\lambda = s^2 \int\limits_0^\infty u^2 h_0(\lambda)\, f(\lambda)\, \mathrm{d}\lambda$$

$$= s^2 \left\{ \int\limits_0^\infty h_2(\lambda, x)\, f(\lambda)\, \mathrm{d}\lambda \right\} = s^2 \left\{ \int\limits_0^x (x - \lambda)\, f(\lambda)\, \mathrm{d}\lambda \right\}$$

$$= s^2 u^2 \, \{ f(x) \} = f . \qquad (46)$$

---

[1]) In case of an arbitrary function $f(x) \in R$, $f(\lambda)$ is put for $f(x)\,|_{x=\lambda}$.

Now if the upper limit of the integral is fixed by a, we get

$$\int_0^a h_0(\lambda)\, f(\lambda)\, d\lambda = s^2 \left\{ \int_0^a (x - \lambda)\, f(\lambda)\, d\lambda \right\}$$

$$= \{ f(x) \} - s^2 \left\{ \int_a^x (x - \lambda)\, f(\lambda)\, d\lambda \right\}$$

$$= \{ f(x) \} - \left(\begin{array}{ll} f(x) & [x > a] \\ 0 & [x \leq a] \end{array} \right) = \left(\begin{array}{ll} f(x) & [x \leq a] \\ 0 & [x > a] \end{array} \right). \tag{47}$$

We define an exponential of distributions by

$$h_0(\lambda) = \, ' \mathrm{e}^{-\lambda s} \, '. \tag{48}$$

But this definition has no meaning unless we show that its association with the classical exponential function $\mathrm{e}^{-\lambda x}$ is justified.

The classical function $f(x) = \mathrm{e}^{-\lambda x}$ may be characterised by

(a) $f(0) = 1$

(b) $f(a) f(b) = f(a + b)$ valid for any exponential function

(c) $f'(x) = -\lambda f(x)$ defining base e.

These properties are still maintained by (48), for

(a) $\mathrm{e}^0 = h_0(0) = \delta$ according to (44);

(b) $\mathrm{e}^{-as}\, \mathrm{e}^{-bs} = h_0(a)\, h_0(b) \overset{(42)}{=} h_0(a + b) = \mathrm{e}^{-(a+b)s}$;

(c) $(\mathrm{e}^{-\lambda s})' = [h_0(\lambda)]' \overset{(45)}{=} -h_{-1}(\lambda) \overset{(41)}{=} -s h_0(\lambda) = -s\, \mathrm{e}^{-\lambda s}$.

On using (48) the formulae (44), (46) and (47) may be written:

$$e^{-\lambda s} f = \left\{ \begin{array}{ll} f(x - \lambda) & [\lambda \leq x < \infty] \\ \\ 0 & [0 \leq x < \lambda] \end{array} \right\} \tag{44a}$$

$$\int_0^\infty e^{-\lambda s} f(\lambda) \, d\lambda = \{ f(x) \} = f \tag{46a}$$

$$\int_0^a e^{-\lambda s} f(\lambda) \, d\lambda = \left\{ \begin{array}{ll} f(x) & [x \leq a] \\ \\ 0 & [x > a] \end{array} \right\}. \tag{47a}$$

Formula (46a) belongs, in principle, to § 4, since it is this one that permits the transformation of any function $\{f(x)\}$ that is integrable in terms of the operator s.

8. Partial differential equations

Before stating some results concerning partial differential equations in general, we shall discuss the possibilities offered by the algebraic distribution theory in the case of the one-dimensional wave equation. The results of § 7 will serve as a basis.

The wave equation[1])

$$y_{xx} = \frac{1}{c^2} y_{tt}, \qquad y = y(x, t) \tag{49}$$

may be reduced to a differential equation in one variable (either x or t) only, the other being algebraised according to

---

[1]) Here y_{xx}, y_{tt} mean $\partial^2 y / \partial x^2, \partial^2 y / \partial t^2$. In § 7 the independent variables were denoted by x, λ while here we use t, x. Note of this should be made when employing equations (44a) and (47a).

(25). Here the method chosen is dependent on the initial conditions of the problem. We give here some examples.

(a) $y(\ ,0) = f(x)$, $y_t(x,0) = 0$.

The algebraic translation of (49) reads as follows

$$c^2 y_{xx}(x) = s^2 y(x) - s f(x)$$

according to (25). This differential equation in one variable may be integrated in the classical sense by varying the constants, since we introduced into K an analysis with respect to x as well as the exponential function (48). We get then

$$\{ y(x,t) \} = y(x) = \varphi(x) \, e^{sx/c} + \psi(x) \, e^{-sx/c}$$

where

$$\varphi(x) = -\frac{1}{2c} \int_a^x f(\xi) \, e^{-s\xi/c} \, d\xi \, ,$$

$$\psi(x) = \frac{1}{2c} \int_b^x f(\xi) \, e^{s\xi/c} \, d\xi \, .$$

Substituting

$$\xi - x \Rightarrow vc \, , \quad d\xi \Rightarrow c \, dv \, , \qquad \int_a^x \Rightarrow \int_{(a-x)/c}^0$$

and

$$x - \xi \Rightarrow wc \, , \quad d\xi \Rightarrow -c \, dw \, , \qquad \int_b^x \Rightarrow \int_{(x-b)/c}^0$$

respectively, we find

$$y(x) = -\frac{1}{2} \int_{(a-x)/c}^0 f(vc + x) \, e^{-sv} \, dv - \frac{1}{2} \int_{(x-b)/c}^0 f(x - wc) \, e^{-sw} \, dw$$

$$= \frac{1}{2} \int\limits_{0}^{(a-x)/c} f(x + vc)\, e^{-sv}\, dv + \frac{1}{2} \int\limits_{0}^{(x-b)/c} f(x - wc)\, e^{-sw}\, dw .$$

In order to make use of (47a) we put

$$f(x + cv) \Rightarrow \tilde{f}(v) , \qquad f(x - cw) \Rightarrow \tilde{\tilde{f}}(w)$$

$$\triangleright \quad y(x, t) = \frac{1}{2} \begin{cases} \tilde{f}(t) & \left[t \leq \dfrac{a - x}{c} \right] + \tilde{\tilde{f}}(t) & \left[t \leq \dfrac{x - b}{c} \right] \\[2ex] 0 & \left[t > \dfrac{a - x}{c} \right] + 0 & \left[t > \dfrac{x - b}{c} \right] . \end{cases}$$

This function is, in general, discontinuous for $t = (x - b)/c$ and $t = (a - x)/c$, that is to say for $x = b + ct$ and $x = a - ct$. It in fact 'jumps' by the values

$$\tfrac{1}{2}\tilde{\tilde{f}}\left(\frac{x - b}{c} \right) = \tfrac{1}{2}f\left(x - c\, \frac{x - b}{c} \right) = \tfrac{1}{2}f(b)$$

and

$$\tfrac{1}{2}\tilde{f}\left(\frac{a - x}{c} \right) = \tfrac{1}{2}f\left(x + c\, \frac{a - x}{c} \right) = \tfrac{1}{2}f(a) .$$

If a continuous solution is looked for then we have to shift these discontinuities to infinity by setting $a = \infty$, $b = -\infty$. Thus we get

$$y(x, t) = \tfrac{1}{2}\, [\tilde{f}(t) + \tilde{\tilde{f}}(t)] = \tfrac{1}{2}\, [f(x + ct) + f(x - ct)]$$

which is in agreement with the classical solution (of d'Alembert).

The classical method is, at least in this example, as direct as the method which we just showed. It is, however, only applicable to the case where continuous solutions are involved[1]).

On the other hand, the distribution method shows to be superior than the classical, each time we have to consider in addition to the initial conditions the limit conditions also. This will be seen by considering such a problem now

(b)
$$y(x, 0) = 0, \quad y_t(x, 0) = 0 \, [x > 0],$$
$$y(0, t) = \sigma(t), \quad \sigma(t) = 0 \, [t < 0] \, .^{2)}$$
(50)

This is the problem of a vibrating string in which the deformation is applied at $x = 0$. We begin with the classical method so that later on a comparison between the two methods can be made.

To this aim let us start from the theorem according to which the general solution of equation (49) can always be reduced to the form

$$y(x, t) = f(x + ct) + g(x - ct)$$

where f and g are arbitrary functions. We may then write, on using the first two conditions in (50)

$$y(x, 0) \equiv 0 \equiv f(x) + g(x) \qquad [x > 0]$$
$$\frac{1}{c} y_t(x, 0) \equiv 0 \equiv f_t(x) - g_t(x) \qquad [x > 0]$$
(51)

---

[1]) The case where the initial function $f(x) = y(x,0)$ is not differentiable arises quite often. In this case we are forced in classical formalism to develop $f(x)$ into a Fourier integral; indeed the existence of a solution then rests on the fact that the integral, being uniformly convergent for a continuous function $f(x)$ only, may be differentiated under the sign of integration.

[2]) $\{\sigma(t)\} \in R$ by the last condition! Consistency of (50) obviously implies $\sigma(0) = 0$.

Hence

$$f(\xi) \equiv f_0 = \text{const.}, \quad g(\xi) \equiv g_0 = \text{const.}, \quad f_0 + g_0 = 0$$

[identically for all arguments $\xi > 0$]. In order to find the functions $f(\xi)$ and $g(\xi)$ for $\xi \leq 0$ one has to make use of the third condition in (50):

$$y(0, t) \equiv \sigma(t) \equiv f(ct) + g(-ct)$$

whence

$$f(ct) + g_0 = 0 \qquad [t < 0]$$

$$f_0 + g(-ct) = \sigma(t) \qquad [t \geq 0]$$

i.e. by substituting ξ for ct and $-ct$ respectively

$$f(\xi) = -g_0 \qquad\qquad [\xi < 0]$$

$$g(\xi) = \sigma\left(-\frac{\xi}{c}\right) - f_0 \qquad [\xi < 0].$$

Now since $f(\xi)$ and $g(\xi)$ are determined for any ξ we can calculate for all $t \geq 0$:

$$y(x, t) = f(x + ct) + g(x - ct)$$

$$= \begin{cases} f_0 & [x > |ct|] \\ f_0 & [|ct| \geq x > -|ct|] \\ -g_0 & [-|ct| \geq x] \end{cases} + \begin{cases} g_0 & [x > |ct|] \\ \sigma\left(-\dfrac{x-ct}{c}\right) - f_0 & [|ct| \geq x > -|ct|] \\ \sigma\left(-\dfrac{x-ct}{c}\right) - f_0 & [-|ct| \geq x] \end{cases} \qquad (52)$$

$$= \begin{cases} 0 & [x > |ct|] \\ \sigma\left(t - \dfrac{x}{c}\right) & [x \leq |ct|] \end{cases}$$

which is a wave propagated to the right with velocity c and of invariable form as given by σ for $x = 0$.

We solve now the same problem (50) but this time by means of the distribution method. We have

$$y_{xx} = \frac{1}{c^2} y_{tt} = \frac{s^2}{c^2} y$$

since

$$y(x, 0) = y_t(x, 0) = 0 .$$

The solution is

$$y(x) = \varphi \, e^{sx/c} + \psi \, e^{-sx/c} ,$$

which is interpreted, according to (44a):

$$y(x,t) = \begin{cases} \varphi\left(t + \dfrac{x}{c}\right) & \left[-\dfrac{x}{c} \leq t < \infty\right] \\ 0 & \left[0 \leq t < -\dfrac{x}{c}\right] \end{cases} + \begin{cases} \psi\left(t - \dfrac{x}{c}\right) & \left[\dfrac{x}{c} \leq t < \infty\right] \\ 0 & \left[0 \leq t < \dfrac{x}{c}\right] . \end{cases}$$

or still, in terms of inequalities in x:

$$y(x, t) = \begin{cases} \varphi\left(t + \dfrac{x}{c}\right) & [\,|ct| < x] \\ \varphi\left(t + \dfrac{x}{c}\right) + \psi\left(t - \dfrac{x}{c}\right) & [x \leq |ct|\,] . \end{cases}$$

From the third condition of (50) it follows that $y(0, t) = \sigma(t) = \varphi(t) + \psi(t)$ for all arguments t of φ and ψ, consequently

$$y(x, t) = \begin{cases} \varphi\left(t + \dfrac{x}{c}\right) & [\,|ct| < x] \\ \varphi\left(t + \dfrac{x}{c}\right) + \sigma\left(t - \dfrac{x}{c}\right) - \varphi\left(t - \dfrac{x}{c}\right) & [x \leq |ct|\,] . \end{cases} \tag{53}$$

This solution is not unique since the function φ itself is not. But the supplementary postulate of the continuity of the solution suffices for us to determine in a unique way the solution (53), for continuity at $x = |ct|$ means

$$y(|ct|, t) = \varphi(t + |t|) + \sigma(t - |t|) - \varphi(t - |t|)$$

$$= \lim_{x > |ct| \to |ct|} y(x, t) = \varphi(t + |t|)$$

from which follows, with $\sigma(0) = 0$,

$$\varphi(t - |t|) = 0,$$

and since this holds for all t:

$$\varphi(\xi) \equiv 0.$$

The unique continuous solution of (50) will therefore be

$$y(x, t) = \begin{cases} 0 & [\,|ct| < x] \\ \sigma\left(t - \dfrac{x}{c}\right) & [x \leq |ct|\,] \end{cases}$$

which corresponds to (52).

When we compare the methods we note that perhaps on the one side the classical method does not look more complicated than that of the distribution. It has, however, a drawback namely the necessity of separating into two the domain of the definition of the functions $f(\xi)$ and $g(\xi)$. As a case in point we shall consider the problem (b) with the new condition that the string be fixed at $x = l$.

(c) $y(x, 0) \equiv 0$, $y_t(x, 0) \equiv 0$ $[0 \leq x < l]$,

$$y(0, t) = \sigma(t), y(l, t) \equiv 0 .   (54)$$

If we are only interested in the movement of the string between $x = 0$ and $x = l$ then the last condition of (54) can be replaced by two others:

$$y(x + 2ln, t) = y(x, t); y(l + x, t) = - y(l - x, t)$$

$$[0 \leq x < l, n = 1, 2, \ldots] .$$

The first of these expressions gives the periodicity $2l$ along x and the second an antisymmetry with respect to $x = l$. Then if a wave σ starts from $x = 0$ at the same time a number of waves σ start from points $x = 2ln$ in both directions. This will cause in the interval $0 \geq x \geq l$ a superposition of an infinite number of solutions (52) of different 'phases' n in $\sigma(2ln + t + x/c)$ according to the points in which the waves were created. In the classical method the calculation of each wave $\sigma(2ln + t + x/c)$ necessitates a distinction in the domain of the variable ξ in f and g starting with

$$0 \leqq x < l - ct < x < l + ct < \ldots ;$$

this rather complicates the situation.

In this problem the method of distributions shows itself to be most convincing because of its logical simplicity. We have, as in (b)

$$y(x) = \varphi \, e^{sx/c} + \psi \, e^{-sx/c}   (55)$$

$$\varphi + \psi = \sigma$$

and furthermore, by considering the last condition of (54),

$$\varphi\, e^{sl/c} + \psi\, e^{-sl/c} = 0.\qquad(56)$$

From (55) and (56) it follows that

$$\varphi = -\frac{e^{-2s/c(l-x)}}{1 - e^{-2sl/c}}\,\sigma$$

$$\psi = \frac{1}{1 - e^{-2sl/c}}\,\sigma$$

$$\triangleright\quad y(x) = \frac{e^{-s(2l-x)/c} + e^{-sx/c}}{1 - e^{-2sl/c}}\,\sigma\,,$$

and on developing

$$\frac{1}{1 - e^{-2sl/c}} = 1 + e^{-2sl/c} + e^{-4sl/c} + \dots$$

$$\triangleright\quad y(x) = (e^{-sx/c} + e^{-s(2l+x)/c} + e^{-s(4l+x)/c} + \dots$$
$$- e^{-s(2l-x)/c} - e^{-s(4l-x)/c} - \dots)\,\sigma$$

so finally according to (44a)

$$y(x,t) = \begin{cases} 0 & \left[t \leq \dfrac{x}{c}\right] \\[2ex] \sigma\left(t - \dfrac{x}{c}\right) & \left[\dfrac{x}{c} < t \leq \dfrac{2l+x}{c}\right] \\[2ex] \sigma\left(t - \dfrac{x}{c}\right) + \sigma\left(t - \dfrac{2l+x}{c}\right) & \left[\dfrac{2l+x}{c} < t \leq \dfrac{4l+x}{c}\right] \\[2ex] \sigma\left(t - \dfrac{x}{c}\right) + \sigma\left(t - \dfrac{2l+x}{c}\right) \\[1ex] \quad + \sigma\left(t - \dfrac{4l+x}{c}\right) & \left[\dfrac{4l+x}{c} < t \leq \dfrac{6l+x}{c}\right] \\[2ex] \text{etc.} \end{cases}$$

$$-\begin{cases} 0 & \left[t \leqq \dfrac{2l-x}{c} \right] \\[2.5ex] \sigma\left(t - \dfrac{2l-x}{c} \right) & \left[\dfrac{2l-x}{c} < t \leqq \dfrac{4l-x}{c} \right] \\[2.5ex] \sigma\left(t - \dfrac{2l-x}{c} \right) + \sigma\left(t - \dfrac{4l-x}{c} \right) & \left[\dfrac{4l-x}{c} < t \leqq \dfrac{6l-x}{c} \right] \\[2.5ex] \text{etc.} \end{cases}$$

We see that the first group of additive terms represent waves progressing to the right with a velocity c and departing simultaneously from all the points $x = 2ln$ whereas the second group of additive terms describes the reflective waves, going towards the left departing from the points $2ln$.

This development is much more simple than the classical one; above all it is the introduction of an exponential function of distributions that has been found to be advantageous. This fact can be verified by solving other differential equations in two variables.

The solution of partial differential equations in more than two independent variables requires a generalisation of § 7 in introducing exponential functions (eventually also logarithms) of several variables. This is possible and in fact has been done. Another point to consider along these lines is the following: Is it possible to algebraise more than one variable? This question is analogous to the possibility of a double Laplace transform the solution of which is beyond the scope of this booklet.

We close with the following two notes:
(1) The distribution method *simplifies* the classical by reducing through algebraisation a system of differential equations with n independent variables to a system of $n - 1$ variables

as well as by simplifying the question of taking limit conditions into account, as shown in example (c).

(2)　The distribution method *generalises* the classical in the sense that it furnishes us with generalised solutions from which the classical solutions follow by way of the supplementary postulate of continuity.

SUBJECT INDEX